EMOTIONAL HAZARDS IN ANIMALS AND MAN

Publication Number 299
AMERICAN LECTURE SERIES®

A Monograph in
AMERICAN LECTURES IN OBJECTIVE PSYCHIATRY

Edited by
WILLIAM HORSLEY GANTT, M.D.
Phipps Psychiatry Clinic
The Johns Hopkins Hospital
Baltimore, Maryland

Emotional Hazards
in Animals
and Man

By

HOWARD S. LIDDELL, Ph.D.

Professor of Psychobiology
Director of the Behavior Farm Laboratory
Cornell University, Ithaca, New York
Formerly, Professor of Physiology
Ithaca Division, Cornell University Medical College
Ithaca, New York

CHARLES C THOMAS · PUBLISHER
Springfield · Illinois · U.S.A.

CHARLES C THOMAS · PUBLISHER

BANNERSTONE HOUSE

301-327 East Lawrence Avenue, Springfield, Illinois, U.S.A.

Published simultaneously in the British Commonwealth of Nations

by

BLACKWELL SCIENTIFIC PUBLICATIONS, LTD., OXFORD, ENGLAND

Published simultaneously in Canada by

THE RYERSON PRESS, TORONTO

Library of Congress Catalog Card Number: 56-11157

Printed in the United States of America

DEDICATED

To my friend and fellow investigator since 1926
W. Horsley Gantt
Behaviorist and Humanist

Preface

IN LENINGRAD, on an August day thirty years ago
Dr. W. Horsley Gantt and I met for the first time.
It was not by accident that we met in Pavlov's laboratory, for both of us were pursuing the same goal;
namely, a first hand practical knowledge of Pavlov's
conditioning method. We believed then, and believe
now, that the persevering use of this powerful and
exact method in the field of experimental medicine
can disclose the biological basis of many fundamental
problems concerning mental health and disease. No
student of psychiatry should neglect to peruse Gantt's
classical monograph on the *Experimental Basis of
Neurotic Behavior* in which our mutual conviction
appears fully justified. In this monograph, the
veteran neurotic dog Nick's case history over a period
of thirteen years is presented in meticulous clinical
detail.

In the Spring of 1923, G. V. Anrep, a former as-
sistant to Pavlov, lectured at Cornell on the conditioned reflex and advised me in the construction of a
small conditioning laboratory for sheep and goats.
Work in this and later in a new laboratory for teaching and research built in 1938 has continued without
interruption to the present. Anrep's lecture, just as
he gave it, is to be found in the first edition of Lovatt
Evans' *Recent Advances in Physiology* published by
Blakiston about 1927.

In concluding his lecture he described the onset of
experimental neurosis in one of Pavlov's dogs whilst
attempting to discriminate a luminous circle, a signal
for food, from a series of ovals more and more nearly

circular, all meaning no food. With this information in mind, I was able to recognize in 1927 the manifestations of experimental neurosis in one of our sheep when subjected to a regimen of arduous conditioning.

At the beginning our subject of investigation was the influence of thyroidectomy on various physiological functions but, since our aim was a better clinical understanding of thyroid function, we were obliged to consider behavior as well. We decided, therefore, to employ Pavlov's conditioning method as a quantitative method for estimating possible deficits in learning or intelligence in sheep and goats thyroidectomized at three weeks of age when their performance was studied over the brief life span of three to five years—less than half the life span of normal animals. However, having unwittingly precipitated an experimental neurosis in one of our "normal control" sheep, we thereafter concentrated more and more on the systematic analysis of Pavlovian conditioning as a stressful procedure inevitably leading to chronic patterns of neurotic behavior.

The year 1929 marked a turning point in the history of our laboratory. Through the good offices of Gantt, I had earlier met in Leningrad, P. S. Kupalov, who as a traveling fellow, worked in our laboratory in Ithaca during the summer of 1929. It was his broad and unbiased appraisal of the details of Pavlov's conditioned reflex investigations then in progress which gave us confidence in the basic importance for medicine of this new and then almost unknown field of research.

In August of that year the International Physiological Congress met in Boston. Gantt, terminating his six years of work in Pavlov's laboratory, came to Boston where he, Pavlov, Kupalov and myself were able to confer pleasantly and at length. Dr. Aldolf Meyer, meanwhile, had encouraged Gantt to establish a conditioning laboratory (the present Pavlovian laboratory) at the Phipps Clinic of the Johns Hopkins Hospital. In May 1955 we celebrated the 25th anniversary of the Pavlovian Laboratory and through the initiative of Gantt organized a new society for the advancement of objective psychiatry.

Class room demonstrations of the performance of sheep and goats, both normal and experimentally neurotic, have been for us a necessary accompaniment of the research from its inception. From 1925 to 1938 this teaching was a part of the course in medical physiology. In 1945, as guest professor at the Institute for Training and Research in Psychoanalysis, Columbia University, I began, at the invitation of its director, Dr. Sandor Rado, demonstrating and discussing our conditioning experiments with the residents in psychiatry.

Finally, in the Spring of 1954, I was invited by Professor Robert Jones, Head of the Department of Psychiatry, Dalhousie University, to deliver six lectures at the Royal Victoria Hospital in Halifax to the psychiatric residents of the Maritime Provinces. The six brief lectures which follow are based upon the material there presented. The invaluable discussions occasioned by my remarks at that time have led to new insights into the significance of investigations, such as Gantt's and my own, for experimental medicine and clinical psychiatry.

Another opportunity to test the efficacy of clinical demonstrations of our animal subjects arose last November. Professor Henry W. Brosin, Director, Western Psychiatric Institute and Clinics, University of Pittsburgh School of Medicine, invited us to demonstrate two experimentally neurotic animals before his residents in psychiatry. We brought from Ithaca to Pittsburgh in the laboratory station wagon, our ram, Robert, and our goat, Brown Billy and spent the day in demonstrating these two "patients" to the physicians at the Institute. These same "patients" are discussed in the lectures which follow.

For many years, in fact since 1937, I have been deeply indebted for the continuing interest, encouragement, and most importantly for the penetrating criticisms of Dr. Frank Fremont-Smith, Medical Director of the Josiah Macy Jr. Foundation. Liberal grants from this Foundation have been crucial in insuring the unbroken continuity of our investigations during peace and war. Continuity, as such, can lead to stagnation. However, the Josiah Macy Jr. Conferences, two of which have met at our laboratory, have given us the benefit of searching and constructive criticism from outstanding investigators in the fields of physiology, clinical psychiatry, sociology and anthropology. The lectures which follow are, therefore, in the nature of a progress report to the Josiah Macy Jr. Foundation and a testimonial to the inspiration of an eminent catalyst of interdisciplinary research in the medical sciences, Dr. Frank Fremont-Smith.

H. S. L.

Table of Contents

EMOTIONAL HAZARDS IN ANIMALS AND MAN

Chapter I

A Clinical Demonstration

LET US PRETEND that we have assembled for a medical staff meeting. Instead of a patient, however, we bring to the clinic for demonstration a seemingly normal Shropshire ram three years of age. He is comfortably restrained within a wooden box about the size of a piano box with the front removed. This demonstration box is mounted upon a movable table. The only restraint of the animal is provided by a web strap about the chest fastened to a vertical rod. Although prevented from kneeling he has free use of his limbs and can shift position at will.

We wheel our "patient" whose name is Robert, into the amphitheater and prepare to demonstrate his peculiarities of behavior. For this purpose a few simple facilities suffice. On an instrument panel behind the box where Robert cannot see it there is a metronome, a door buzzer, door bell, and a source of 60 cycle current, the voltage of which can be varied but for our "patient" 6 volts or less will be sufficient. The wires of a flexible cable terminating in battery clips lead from the panel to the animal's right foreleg. Two moistened pieces of cloth the size of shoe laces are wrapped around this limb just above the forefoot. The battery clips from the cable are attached to these cloth electrodes through which a brief electrical stimulus can be applied to the skin of the sheep's foreleg at the demonstrator's convenience.

The demonstration now begins and the following details of behavior are noted. As Robert is wheeled into the amphitheater he is alert but seemingly unperturbed. He glances at the spectators but when a bucket of oats is placed before him he eats at once and continues while the electrodes are fastened to his foreleg. When the food is removed he continues to stand quietly and does not appear to be disturbed by conversation among the spectators or the arrival of late comers. His breathing is slow and regular at 41 per minute. He does not bleat and exhibits almost no movement of limbs, head, or ears. One gets the impression that in these strange surroundings he is too quiet and composed.

The demonstrator now discusses Robert's case with the audience for ten minutes and at the end of this period the respiratory rate is still practically unchanged at 40 per minute. Moreover, if the heart rate is being determined electrically during the discussion period it will be found to remain quite steady from 60 to 78 beats per minute.

The demonstrator proceeds to elicit a well established conditioned response. The metronome starts clicking once a second. At the first click Robert abruptly raises his head and pricks up his ears. Then he deliberately lowers his head and slightly crouches with forelegs extended. At the third or fourth metronome beat he executes a small, precise flexion of the right foreleg followed by a series of deliberate unhurried flexions of increasing amplitude and vigor. Coinciding with the 11th beat of the metronome a brief electrical stimulus is delivered to the rhythmically flexing foreleg. In response to this electrical startle stimulus Robert executes a brief but vehement flexion of the foreleg reminding one of the withdrawal of the hand at the bite of an insect. Following this rapid, perfunctory flexion, our "patient" immediately resumes his quiet, alert pose.

At this point the metal clips are detached from the cloth electrodes on Robert's foreleg and the demonstrator invites one of the audience to dip his fingers in salt solution and firmly grip the battery clips between his thumb and fingers. He is repeatedly given the same electrical stimulus to which Robert had reacted so vehemently. However the human subject feels either nothing or at most a barely perceptible tingle.

However, among college students witnessing this demonstration we always find a few who are loth to test the electrical stimulus. Some of these upon urging will submit to the test. They respond to the current almost as vigorously as Robert with an exaggerated shudder and grimace.

If such a sensitive individual now joins hands with two others who cannot feel or barely feel the current as a tingle and each of the insensitive individuals seizes one of the electrodes firmly in the hand then when the brief electrical current passes through all three individuals the middle sensitive man will give his usual vigorous shudder and grimace.

The extreme variability from person to person of the reaction to the passage of even very weak electric current through the skin is well known as is the similar variability in aversion to hypodermic injection or venipuncture. Here, we are concerned not with the physical characteristics of the stimulus but rather with the meaning of the stimulus for the individual as inferred from his observable behavior. It has been discovered, for example, that the patient's reaction to the administration of ACTH or cortisone is in part determined by his knowledge or suspicion of how these substances may affect him. There is no doubt from our observation of hundreds of sheep and goats that the mildest electrical stimulation of the skin of the limbs is interpreted as gravely threatening. Such a minimal startle stimulus to the forelimb of the untrained animal leads to vehement aggression or attempts to escape through leaping or struggling if this is physically possible.

We again attach the electrodes to Robert's foreleg and proceed with the demonstration. Twenty minutes have now elapsed and the respiratory rate has increased from 40 to 56 per minute. The respirations are visibly deeper. The metronome is now set at 120 beats per minute. When the rapid clicking begins the "patient" raises his head and pricks up his ears as before. As the clicking continues for 10 seconds, however, he stands rigidly with head raised but with no movement of the limbs. This signal is *not* followed by shock. Two telltale signs indicate that he is not quiescent during this auditory experience even though there is no withdrawal of the foreleg. His breathing becomes rapid and labored in addition to which a marked cremasteric reflex can be clearly observed.

After two or three minutes we sound the door buzzer to which our animal reacts as he did to the metronome clicking once a second, with deliberate flexion to the customary brief electrical stimulation.

During another pause of a few minutes our animal stolidly awaits what may next occur but hastened and irregular breathing betrays his continuing perturbation. Now we ring the door bell. Robert answers by brusque raising of the head and tensing of the motionless limbs with labored respiration. His behavior tells the spectators what to expect since no shock follows this signal.

Robert has now answered four of our questions correctly and unequivocally. In reply to the slow metronome and door buzzer he clearly indicated that he expected a shock to the right foreleg. To the fast metronome and door bell his answer was a definitely "no shock coming." In spite of the precision of the positive and negative motor responses it was clear that all four signals elected emotional reactions and that *the negative signals were the more disturbing even though no shock followed*.

During three years of laboratory education, which began at three months of age, Robert has become a virtuoso at discriminating metronome rates. He was first taught that the metronome at 60 beats per minute was always followed by shock to the foreleg. Then during the early months of training he learned that the metronome at 120 beats per minute was never followed by this electrical stimulation, as has been shown in our demonstration. The discrimination between the positive signal, metronome 60, and faster rates signalling no shock was made progressively more difficult in succeeding months. Negative responses were elaborated to the following metronome rates: 100, 92, 84, 78 and finally 72 beats per minute as signals that no shock was to follow.

Since we propose to limit our demonstration to one hour we need not test Robert's reaction to each of these negative or no-shock metronome rates but only to three of increasing difficulty; namely, 92, 78, and 72 beats per minute.

To conclude this imaginary demonstration which has now lasted for 30 minutes, we shall proceed as follows: The duration of each metronome signal will vary from 3 to 15 seconds and the signals will follow one another at irregular intervals of 2 to 5 minutes, thus preventing the sheep from reacting to any temporal cues other than the metronome rates themselves. This variability of signal duration and of interval between signals was maintained during training. Moreover, positive and negative signals were always given in random order.

As Robert stands awaiting our pleasure he no longer gives the impression of imperturability which we noticed half an hour earlier. His respiratory rate has now increased from 40 to 90 per minute. Breathing movements are labored and audible. He occasionally sighs or yawns and there is much nose licking. During the previous buzzer signal grinding of the teeth was clearly audible and from now on is to be listened for at every conditioned stimulus, positive or negative. However, there is little movement of head or limbs in the intervals between signals.

It is unnecessary to describe Robert's reactions to the next six signals since they are as stereotyped as those which were observed during the first half hour of our demonstration.

During the ensuing six tests, spaced two to five minutes apart, Robert reacts correctly to metronome

60 positive, metronome 92 negative, metronome 60 positive, metronome 78 negative, metronome 60 positive, and finally, metronome 72 negative. As the negative, or no-shock metronome signals approach more and more closely to the positive rate of 60 per minute our animal's discomfort at the negative signals rapidly mounts. At the sound of the metronome signalling no shock the body visibly tenses while the forelimbs are rigidly extended giving the appearance of the forefeet being glued to the platform. When the last negative signal, metronome 72, is given the respiratory rate abruptly rises from 94 to 139 per minute.

Before terminating this demonstration we have one more test to make. Just now our sheep successfully, but with obvious effort, refrained from flexing his right foreleg while the metronome at 72 beats per minute sounded for 10 seconds. He correcty anticipated that no shock would follow. Allowing our subject a cooling off-period of 5 minutes we sound the metronome at 60 per minute for 10 seconds followed immediately by a shock to the foreleg. In spite of his labored and irregular breathing Robert deliberately crouches and executes a series of precise flexions of the foreleg terminated by a brief maximal flexion at the shock. This skilled, stereotyped conditioned response differs in no essential feature from his reaction at the beginning of the demonstration almost an hour ago. One is reminded of the deliberate wind-up and pitch of the nearly exhausted pitcher in the 9th or 10th inning of a tied baseball game.

After a waiting period of four minutes we once more sound the metronome at 72 beats per minute for

10 seconds. Robert again successfully refrains from flexing his foreleg thus correctly anticipating that no shock is to follow.

Now for the first time during the demonstration we pause *for only one minute* between signals. Exactly one minute after metronome 72 has ceased we sound the metronome at 60 beats per minute and for the first time during the hour Robert fails dramatically in interpreting the signal most familiar to him—the signal, which, since the beginning of his training three years ago, has always meant shock. As the clicking begins at once a second he freezes with forelegs stiffly extended and with signs of respiratory distress. In fact, he duplicates his reaction to the just preceding difficult negative signal, metronome 72. At the end of 10 seconds the sound of metronome 60 is terminated by the usual shock to the right foreleg. However, Robert's reaction to this mild unconditioned stimulus is quite unusual. He leaps violently upward with both forelegs in the air but then immediately resumes a tense pose.

The demonstration is over and we may dismiss the "patient."

Let us now attempt to interpret certain details of the apparently ordinary behavior of this seemingly normal, three year old ram which we have just been observing. These proposed interpretations will suggest for later discussion definite implications for psychiatry. Such implications will be explicitly stated from our point of view as they arise in the analysis of the experimental findings.

In the course of 34 years spent in the experimental investigation of the behavior of sheep, goat, pig, and dog, we have been forced to make a basic assumption. This assumption is that *there are no commonplaces of behavior* to be observed either in animals or men. The most ordinary or trivial instances of behavior will usually prove upon experimental analysis to be most complexly determined. Even in sheep and goat the determining factors must often be traced back to birth itself as we shall shortly try to show.

First, consider our animal's apparent imperturbability as he was wheeled in for the demonstration. His deportment did not suggest his confinement within the testing cabinet was of itself a stressful experience apart from the conditioned stimuli which followed. It should be noted in passing that he has been thus confined for several hundred test periods during his three years of training.

However, two simple experiments show that this seemingly innocuous, self-imposed restraint is notably stressful. For the first experiment the animal is brought to the laboratory at 10 A.M. and placed in the demonstration cabinet but nothing further is done. His respiratory rate at the end of 5 minutes is 45 per minute but within the hour excitement steadily mounts as indicated by increasingly frequent and abrupt movements of the trained foreleg, occasional grinding of the teeth, and steadily increasing respiratory rate. When released at the end of an hour the rate is 102 per minute. The second experiment begins at 2 P.M. The sheep is brought from the barnyard and placed in the demonstration cabinet for another hour without tests. But now respiration at the end of 5 minutes is 115 per minute in contrast to 45 per minute at the beginning of the morning session. At the end of this second hour in addition to increasing frequency of limb movement, breathing is labored and audible. During the last 5 minute period the respiratory rate is 142 per minute. Since this animal had not been running or struggling and the time was early June after the sheep had been shorn the high respiratory rate at the beginning of the afternoon session can be attributed neither to exercise nor thermo-regulation.

The sheep's perturbation is clearly a manifestation of anxious expectation which perseverates in the barnyard during the recess between morning and afternoon sessions. What is to happen next? The animal has imposed upon himself an abnormally severe restraint. No matter what impends he can neither fight nor flee. The not uncomfortably tight restraining strap around the sheep's chest is only a reminder of its fruitless attempts as a lamb to escape from the box during the early days of training. From long experience its present attitude must of necessity be fatalistic.

In a similar situation we have repeatedly observed a 400 pound sow lustily squeal while shaking her foreleg at the signal for shock. She could easily have demolished the frame anchoring the harness by which she was restrained and attacked the experimenter standing nearby. Yet during a year of almost daily tests this never happened, although she did attack the experimenter one day in the pasture.

These observations direct attention to the central problem of anxiety. In further discussion of the sheep's behavior as disclosed by the demonstration we shall be concerned with the animal origins of human anxiety and of psychic trauma.

Returning to the discussion, Robert's response to the first signal given during our demonstration, although commonplace enough, is not what it seems. At the clicking of the metronome once a second he instantly raised his head but then slowly and deliberately crouched before executing a series of precise and unhurried flexions of the right foreleg. Moreover, near the end of the hour, despite his rapid and disturbed breathing, his reaction to a repetition of this same metronome signal was equally precise and unhurried.

We had always assumed that these flexions of the forelimb were but localized avoidance movements, although they clearly could not serve this purpose since shock to the leg always followed. Ten years ago Nolan Lewis suggested to us that the sheep was really attempting to run away. However, due to the self-imposed restraint occasioned by the circumstances of his training he was *symbolically running away* with his right foreleg only. Subsequent experiments with more than 100 sheep and goats have confirmed Lewis' conjecture.

A young lamb or kid is confined in a room 10 feet square, with complete freedom of locomotion. A flexible cable suspended from the center of the ceiling is attached to a web strap around the little animal's chest. Electrodes from this cable deliver a brief and feeble shock to one foreleg at the experimenter's convenience. As a signal of the approaching shock the lights in the room are dimmed for 10 seconds at the end of which the lights come on again and the shock is delivered. Twenty darkness signals are given at each session and they are spaced two minutes apart.

At the first experience of the weak electric shock to the foreleg the subject, either lamb or kid, leaps upward and dashes across the room, sometimes climbing against the wall. After 5 to 15 darkness signals preceding shock the animal's response to the dimming of the lights is literally an attempt to escape the situation by walking rapidly and then breaking into a run just before the shock is delivered. At the shock it leaps upward but then abruptly quiets. Later in training it may anticipate the signal by starting to walk a few seconds before the lights are dimmed. As in Robert's case, however, the little animal's attempts to escape are futile since the shock always follows.

This locomotor pattern now passes through the following inevitable phases: First, the animal instead of walking, then running in the normal manner in response to the signal adopts a characteristic jerky pattern of progression. It takes a few mincing steps forward, then backward. At this stage it remains standing against the wall in one corner of the room during the intervals between signals. Finally, it ceases locomotion altogether and at the signal merely executes the precise rhythmical flexions of one foreleg which we observed in our demonstration of Robert's conditioned behavior.

In order properly to understand this sheep's responses to the various positive and negative conditioned stimuli their biological significance must be explored. All of our experimental findings lead to a conclusion with significant implications for psychiatry.

We now believe that each and every conditionel response in sheep, goat, pig or dog whether positive or negative exemplifies a refinement and elaboration, or even chronic distortion, of the crude fight or flight pattern studied by Cannon in his analysis of the emergency reaction.

I doubt that Pavlov ever fully realized, if at all, that the conditioned reflexes which he investigated for so many years in the dog were such episodes of emotional behavior differing in no fundamental respect from the reaction of a cat barked at by a dog. Although during the last period of his career he was mainly concerned with the chronic emotional disorders of his conditioned dogs (which he unfortunately called experimental neuroses), I am convinced that he failed to appreciate the fact that his classical conditioning procedure inevitably leads, if long enough continued, to emotional bankruptcy and chronically disabling behaviors in the experimental animal. In our laboratory we have succeeded by this classical method in precipitating such chronic emotional disorders (or experimental neuroses) in sheep, goat, pig and dog thus validating through comparative study Pavlov's original results based on the dog only.

If we adopt the interpretation of conditioned behavior just proposed certain puzzling features of Robert's behavior during our demonstration become clearer.

We have yet to explain his seemingly paradoxical behavior in discriminating the metronome at 72 beats per minute as a signal for no shock from the closely similar rate of 60 as a signal for shock. You will remember that he successfully, though with obvious effort, refrained from flexing his leg in response to metronome 72. Then, after a cooling-off period of 5 minutes he executed the usual precise flexions to the postive rate of 60.

On the other hand, when at the end of our demonstration we sounded metronome 72 for 10 seconds without shock and *after the lapse of only one minute* changed to metronome 60, Robert remained frozen in position with no trace of the expected flexion response to the signal for shock.

Why does he correctly discriminate between these closely similar rates when they are separated by a 5-minute pause but is unable to do so when only a minute elapses between 72 and 60?

In making a conventional psycho-physical judgment as in comparing lifted weights A and B the judgment becomes more accurate as the interval between lifting A and lifting B is reduced to a matter of seconds. Robert's best performance occurs when the metronome rates to be compared are separated by a number of minutes.

It seems obvious that *our sheep is concerned with problems of emotional control rather than of cognitive achievement.* We believe it fallacious to make a dichotomy of thought versus emotion. Rather, thinking is at one extreme of a continuum and emotional expression and control at the other. The behavior we have been discussing lies near the emotional end of this continuum.

At the beginning we described Robert as a seemingly normal ram. We discovered quite by accident that he was sexually disabled as a consequence of his earlier stressful training. This discovery leads us to

believe that we can experimentally induce the homo-
logue of Freudian repression in the male of this
simple mammalian species. The circumstances leading to this new area of investigation were as follows:

In former years we characterized as experimental
neurosis only the more dramatic manifestations of
chronic loss of emotional control; either extreme
lethargy and passivity or extreme vigilance with bouts
of uncontrollable agitation both in laboratory and
pasture. At that time we were not concerned (but
should have been) with the areas of sexual behavior
and reproduction. As a matter of convenience our
experimental flock of sheep and goats was limited
to females and castrates. Normal males were borrowed
for the breeding season only.

In consequence, Robert was the first normal male
we had ever trained from youth. We took it as a
matter of course, therefore, that when he began his
training in conditioning at three months that his
behavior during the daily tests should be similar to
that of female lambs or castrates at the same age. After
a few sessions of mild struggling he gave up bleating
and assumed the familiar quiet pose of the trained
animal between the conditioned signals. His conditioned leg flexions became as precise and unhurried
as those of the females in training.

Unfortunately, Robert died of pneumonia at 5
years of age. Since he was our most valuable animal
for demonstration purposes we attempted to condition in the usual way a sexually mature ram a year
old. It could not be done. Our signals and shocks
elicited only the familiar fighting behavior of the ram.
At the signal he lowered his lead and executed a

series of rapid pawing movements first with one fore-leg, then the other. Then he vigorously butted the wall in front of him and if we approached his head he directed his attack at us. Only a very occasional feeble flexion movement of the usual conditioned type was elicited by the signal for shock. The shock itself in addition to the forced flexion was followed by the fighting pattern of rapid pawing and butting. Another year old ram was chosen for conditioning with the same result.

We may tentatively conclude that in Robert's case normal sexuality was repressed. We never observed the male fighting pattern in him either in laboratory or pasture. There is also reason to believe that he was incapable of normal mating behavior. However, we are now attempting to analyze this simple type of repression of sexuality in other young rams as a consequence of the conditioning procedures previously described.

Chapter II

The Biological Basis of Psychic Trauma

PERHAPS the most intriguing problem for the investigator of animal behavior is the biological basis of psychic trauma. No one believes that susceptibility to mental injury is an unique human frailty. The gun-shy dog, the spoiled race horse are familiar examples of disabling behavior. A basic semantic problem can be avoided by admitting that there cannot be a *psychodynamics of animal behavior,* at least within the technical limitations of the term as commonly employed in psychiatry. No matter how convinced one may be that his dog shares his simple feelings and thoughts, this conviction cannot become a matter of scientific demonstration.

Since the generalizations of contemporary psychodynamics based upon the investigations of Freud have been derived from the labors of the psychiatrist in consulting room and clinic and involve the exercise of highly developed skills of verbal communication between physician and patient, it seems superfluous to devise experiments in the field of animal behavior, where verbal communication is lacking, which purport to validate these generalizations.

The psychiatrist will properly point out, however, that he is forced to investigate the behavior of the non-speaking psychotics where he must rely upon

19

those subtle and inconspicuous alterations of posture, movement, secretion and blood flow which his observational sensitivity reveals to him. Such meticulous observation is no less exhausting for the investigator of animal behavior than for the psychiatrist observing his patient's behavior in the clinical setting.

This shared experience of exhaustion from effort expended in deciphering the meaning of behavior gives greatest assurance that psychiatrist and behaviorist are converging upon a common goal and that *they mean business.* "Man is by nature metaphysical and proud" (as Claude Bernard once said) hence theories of behavior will come and go. But by conquering narcissism both behaviorist and psychiatrist can continue the uninterrupted labor of observation. Instead of expending time and print in refuting the other's theories, it behooves each to familiarize himself with the other's findings in order to build a secure bridge from animal to man.

One approach to the problem of psychic trauma from the biological viewpoint may be illustrated by a demonstration recently given for our guests at a medical conference. A mother goat and her twins 10 days of age were brought to the laboratory. The mother and one twin were confined in a bare room 10 ft. square. The other twin was isolated in a like room next door. Each twin was allowed complete freedom of movement but electrodes to the right foreleg were connected with a flexible cable suspended from the center of the ceiling. By means of a central timing device both little animals, each in its own room, were simultaneously subjected to the monotonous schedule already described of lights dimmed for

10 seconds followed by shock and 20 such signals each reinforced by the inevitable shock were spaced 2 minutes apart. We observed the deportment of each kid through a one-way screen. The onset of conditioning was observed to occur as detailed in our earlier discussion.

Both little animals became progressively quieter as the tests continued, moving but little to signal and shock. When the schedule of 20 signals was completed, the kids were left undisturbed with lights on for the next 45 minutes. After the last signal both kids were seen lying on the floor with head pressed against it. The kid with the mother was lying close beside her.

The quietly resting kids reminded one of the puppy or baby suddenly falling asleep while at play. But as usual in attempting to interpret behavior this appearance of quiet rest could not be taken at face value.

Now at approximately 10 minute intervals the following test was made. The experimenter approached each room in turn, quietly opened the door and, standing on the threshold, loudly clapped his hands. Although the resting pose of both kids appeared to be identical, the loud hand clapping disclosed a striking difference between them. The kid lying beside its mother promptly raised its head and pricked up its ears. Its twin in the adjoining room remained completely unresponsive to the noise. Not so much as a flick of movement was observed—no opening of the eyes, no movement of the ears. Only at the end of the 45 minute after-period did this solitary kid for the first time sluggishly come to attention at the loud clapping.

How did the presence of the mother "protect" her kid against the exhausting effects of the monotonously reiterated darkness signals each followed by shock? The isolated twin next door was obviously much more affected by this seemingly innocuous procedure.

In experiments extending over the past six years we have imposed this rigid time schedule of darkness signals upon both lambs and kids starting at 3 weeks of age where the daily training schedule was continued for 50 days. In every case the lamb or kid trained in the room with its mother showed no detectable abnormalities of behavior, while the isolated animal exhibited the gradual onset of strikingly abnormal behavior, either rigid immobility or complete passivity in the experimental room.

In order to arrive at an understanding of the mother's role in "protecting" her young against the *contrived* stresses of our laboratory training procedures we have found it necessary to go back to birth itself.

When a patient tells the doctor how he feels, he uses the words he knows and usually tries to explain what is wrong. It is the physician's business to interpret what is told him by questioning based upon skilled diagnostic procedures. The situation is much the same when the behaviorist questions his experimental animal by giving the positive and negative signals with which training has made it familiar. When the lamb or kid is isolated during the test hour, it clearly portrays its perturbation. But when tested in the presence of its mother, it appears to be at ease even though the mother is lying in another part of the room grooming herself and seemingly paying no atention to her young. We say that the young is "protected" by the mother's presence and might let the matter rest there. But such expressions as maternal protection, over-protection or rejection do not further our understanding as to what is really going on between the mother at ease and seemingly oblivious of her young and the lamb or kid, perhaps in another part of the room, reacting with precision to the experimenter's signals and exhibiting a carefree interest in its surroundings during the intervals between signals.

The young animal is being "protected" by its mother's presence but what is this protection? *What is really going on?* As just mentioned, it becomes apparent that something is going on when we directly compare the deportment of the isolated twin with the protected twin during stressful training. Not only so. Resumption of a similarly stressful regimen when these animals have reached maturity shows that an injury has been inflicted upon the solitary little animal, the enduring effects of which have incapacitated it in adjusting to the situations encountered in its adult life in laboratory and pasture.

These experiments with the protected and unprotected little animals when they have reached maturity will be recounted later. At the moment we are interested in discovering by what specific means the mother's presence counterbalances the stress imposed upon the little animal by our conditioning routine. She seems to be doing nothing which suggests protective activity during the test periods. But what has she *specifically* done to protect her newborn during its earliest days?

In order to answer this question we have found it necessary as we have just said, to go back to birth itself. During the past five years the intricate transactions between mother and newborn sheep and goat from the beginning of parturition through the first few days of life have been recorded and analyzed with the aid of moving pictures where possible. Only in this way, we believed, would it be possible to arrive at an understanding of the mother's role in protecting her young from the experimentally arranged stresses of our laboratory experiments.

For present purposes, however, brief mention of a few details of the maternal behavior to be observed must suffice. Following parturition the mother goat must do a number of essential things during the first few days of her kid's life if it is to survive. Each of these activities may for many reasons be so inadequate as to retard the development or even endanger the life of her newborn. First, it must seek and be guided to the nursing position. During this highly complex operation many failures may occur before the kid finds the mother's teat. Sometimes when the normal processes have been interfered with, human intervention may be necessary. Then the mother must recognize and respond to the cry of her own kid. The kid must correspondingly, be able to find its mother and come when she calls. Finally, she must maintain a situation in which her kid may safely play and develop normal adventurous activities (the active aspect of vigilance). To achieve this purpose she butts other goats or kids interfering with the play of her own young.

Dr. Helen Blauvelt describes an experiment in

which she interfered with the mother's normal maternal activities. The course of this experiment was recorded in moving pictures and together with her notes taken at the time constitute an adequate permament record of the data.

She describes this simple experiment as follows.

"A mother goat and her hour-old twins had been isolated until the mother ceased the usual constant checking of the identities of her offspring. One twin was white, the other had conspicuous black and white markings. While the mother was eating with her back to the twins, the black and white one was removed and another kid similiar in coloring and size was substituted. The substitute kid, which had been rubbed with this foster mother's afterbirth, was five days old. It exhibited rapid movements and violent play patterns. Normally, an hour old kid is protected by its mother's intervention from all violent contact with other kids. Often, at this age the mother allows no contact between her young and other animals.

"This mother behaved as if she did not realize that the substitution had been made. As usual in the case of a mother with twins she made no move to protect either from the violence of the other. Both mother and true twin oriented to the rapid movements of the "substitute twin," which completely claimed their attention. The mother called the substitute constantly, followed it, smelled it, licked it, protected it from other goats, and permitted it to nurse. She did not feed her own twin, the white kid, during the hour-and-three-quarters period of the substitution. The white twin attempted to follow the substitute twin, often losing its mother in so doing.

"Since the play movements of a five-day-old kid include violently aggressive activities, the little white kid was constantly butted and pushed around. The moving picture of this experiment shows the little white kid shrinking away after these rough contacts. But then, forced to orient to these movements of its partner, it quickly sought further contact with this older, active "substitute twin." Normally protected by its mother, the white twin had no adequate defensive behavior with which to meet this situation. Not safe near its mother, the little white twin was without a safe place."

When the goat mother is taking her ease in the laboratory room while her kid is being subjected to the usual conditioning tests why is her presence there reassuring to her offspring? To repeat our earlier question, *what is really going on?* The answer must be that it is not what the mother is presently doing. It is what she has done in relation to her young since its birth. In the language of conditioning, her presence is a *signal* that all is well.

This statement is supported by many observations such as the following. Many kids at three weeks of age, especially during the earlier test periods, seek close physical contact with the mother. For example, when the lights are dimmed as a signal for shock, the kid will run to its mother lying on the floor and jump upon her at the shock and then lie down pressing its body close against her's until the next darkness signal. Or, if the mother is standing, the little animal will crowd itself between her and the wall.

"Maternal protection" is not a magical formula. It is, instead, the designation of an intricate social process—a series of behavioral manifestations, each of which must be scrutinized under the specific conditions eliciting it.

Freud dramatically speaks of the psychic trauma inflicted in childhood remaining as a scar upon the personality for life. Is it possible to demonstrate correspondingly grave consequences of mental injury inflicted upon young animals such as lamb and kid? The answer is definitely "yes."

In one experiment twin lambs (castrated males) were subjected to one of our standard stressful conditioning regimens. As previously described, the daily test consisted of 20 darkness signals each followed by shock where the signals were repeated every 2 minutes. One twin was, as usual, tested in the presence of its mother, the other in isolation. The experiment was terminated after 32 days of training. The lambs were then returned to the pasture with their mother and were not brought to the laboratory again. Yet in spite of the favorable circumstances of uninterrupted life with the flock, the twin previously trained in isolation died at 10 months of age. The twin "protected" by its mother during the same stressful conditioning was still alive and in good health at 1½ years.

By the 22nd day of testing the isolated twin was already exhibiting in the laboratory striking abnormalities of behavior later to be described in discussing experimental neurosis. Moreover, on the next day when the mother was led on leash to the laboratory this lamb for the first time failed to follow its mother and twin to the laboratory as it had done on all previous occasions. It was already "mentally ill" as judged by its failure to follow mother and twin brother in the normal manner. Our adult experimentally neurotic sheep exhibit similarly damaged gregariousness in their flock contacts.

In order to simplify the experimental situation it had become standard practice in our laboratory to begin the conditioning of sheep and goats at three months of age or older. From three months on we no longer need be concerned with the mother's presence or absence. The young animal maintains emotional control when trained in isolation quite as well as in the presence of other members of its species. This matter will be discussed in the next chapter.

Since various conditioning procedures based upon the animal's self-imposed restraint inevitably led to experimental neuroses, these chronic emotional disorders early became the focus of our experimental studies. However, the observations of René Spitz on the dire effects of lack of mothering on babies in an orphanage suggested to us a new approach to the problem of emotional disorders in sheep and goat. The impairment of all aspects of development in the mother-deprived orphange babies he designated as *hospitalism*. Experiments on the role of maternal protection against the stresses of conditioning in lamb and kid were undertaken to discover whether behavioral impairments corresponding to those described by Spitz could be demonstrated in these immature animals. The abnormal passivity and untimely death of the isolated male lamb described above is but one of a large number of cases of impairment homologous to hospitalism which we have observed in recent years in both lambs and kids.

But suppose that lambs or kids which have been subjected to the stresses of conditioning in the absence of the mother are then turned out to pasture and reach maturity without further testing? Will it be possible to demonstrate at this later time that traces of their earlier traumatic experience still persist? Will they, in consequence, be less able to meet the grueling stress of a more severe conditioning routine than will their more fortunate siblings who were protected by the mother's presence during youthful conditioning?

Although these questione pose a formidable problem, it is a simpler one than the psychiatrist is forced to consider in his daily practice. In a different context, Abram Kardiner contrasts the simpler problem of the behaviorist with the more complex one confronting the psychiatrist. "How many ways are there to hit a nail on the head?" and "How many ways are there to get along with father?"

The problem as just stated was suggested six years ago by John Romano during a visit to our laboratory. His surmise, namely, that definite evidences of psychic trauma sustained during stressful training in youth by the isolated little animal could be demonstrated in maturity has proved to be correct.

It is highly significant that the surmises of experienced psychiatrists such as Nolan Lewis and John Romano have led us to definite experimental validation of their hunches. To test Romano's hypothesis the following experiment (one of several in progress) has been completed.

Four pairs of twin goats of the same sex were selected, the males being castrated soon after birth. One twin of each pair was separted from the mother at

birth and raised in an orphanage outside the laboratory where these kids were confined within a small
fenced enclosure. Here they were unable to see the
rest of the flock, either sheep or goats. They were fed
from a milk pail supplied with nipples and were
cared for by the attendants. The other twin of each
pair was raised with its mother in the barn and out
at pasture with the rest of the flock.

When the kids were 3 weeks of age they were tested
daily for 50 days on the schedule just described. Each
test period included 20 darkness signals of 10 seconds'
duration followed by shock with signals spaced 2
minutes apart. One twin of each pair was tested in the
presence of its mother. The other kid was brought
directly from the orphanage and completely isolated
in the laboratory room, the experimenter observing it
through a one-way screen.

The same striking differences during the course of
conditioning between the behavior of the isolated kid
and the one in the room with its mother were observed as had previously been seen in the case of the
twin lambs. The progressive curtailment of locomotion in the isolated animal during the test hour from
day to day was most pronounced. The lonely little
animal after a few days of training became completely
immobilized in one corner of the room. At this stage
it exhibited pronounced lethargy and lack of muscular tone. The experimenter, when he entered the
room, could handle it as he wished without resistance.

At the end of 50 daily training sessions, during
which each kid had been subjected to 1,000 darkness
signals each followed by shock and separated by 2
minute intervals with 20 signals per day, the 4 kids

trained in isolation were returned to their orphanage. The other four kids were returned to the flock as before.

After a vacation of two years the four pairs of kids, now adult, were again brought to the laboratory daily for retesting in an unusually stressful conditioning situation. Four of the goats had lived the normal life of the flock in barn and pasture. The other four had been raised in the orphanage for a year and were then put out to pasture. During this long interim none of the eight goats had been subjected to any kind of laboratory test.

Now, at the end of two years did the early experience of the orphan goats when placed in isolation in the waxing and waning, monotonously anxious waiting situation of the conditioning laboratory have any demonstrable effect on their adult behavior?

Only one retest situation need be described. The other retests gave similar results. Four goats were brought to the laboratory and restrained, by straps, against one wall. Due to their former habit of self-imposed restraint the mature animals did not struggle to escape as untrained goats would have done. The movements of the trained foreleg of each of the four animals were simultaneously recorded on a kymograph in an adjoining room.

In this situation the four mature goats were subjected to a 10 second darkness signal followed by shock every 6 minutes for 2 hours—*twice as long as the usual test period to which they had been subjected* at 3 weeks of age. Every day, 7 days a week for 24 days the four goats—two originally trained with the mother and two trained in isolation—were set the arduous task of remaining in the laboratory for two hours and being forced to wait exactly six minutes between successive signals.

Within a few days of the beginning of the new tests a clear difference was apparent to the experienced observer between the two orphans trained in isolation and the two goats trained with the mother and protected by her presence during the original stressful conditioning. Near the completion of this 24 day retest period the differences between them were so striking as to be apparent to a casual visitor to the laboratory. The two specific differences which could be readily quantified were as follows: first, the frequency of impatient, fidgety or fretful movements of the trained foreleg during the six minutes of waiting between signals; and second, the number of signals during which the goat was "too slow on the ball" and failed to flex its foreleg before the shock.

In the protected goats the fidgety movements kept going at about the same tempo through the twenty-four days of testing. On the other hand, the orphan goats began by being as fidgety as their controls but as the stressful conditioning continued, these impatient movements of the foreleg sharply decreased. The orphans seemed to become browbeaten and to give up.

Between the first day and the last day of training (the twenty-fourth day) there was a total of 400 signals —a signal every 6 minutes. The protected pair missed 25% of the day's signals on the first day and they continued to miss about 25% of the signals to the end; that is, they did not get the foreleg up before the shock. On the other hand, the deprived, orphaned pair showed steady deterioration in the stability of the conditioned response. They began, as the protected pair did, by missing 25% of the signals at the start, but very soon they were missing more and more signals each day. By the end of the twenty-four day period they were failing to react soon enough to 45% of each day's signals, the shocks taking them unaware.

During the later days of testing they were passing into a state of pronounced lethargy. At the stage where the animals were succumbing to the influence of the continuing and severe stress of training, they became quite inert. The experimenter could approach such a disabled goat and move him around as he pleased. It is as if these animals lacked the muscular tonus necessary to be on the alert for slight environmental changes. Their vigilance had become blunted. They had given up reacting to the familiar signals *and to much else besides.*

Chapter III

The Meaning of Pain and Fear

A<small>NY</small> <small>EXPERIENCE</small> may be colored by pain and fear. Although thresholds of stimuli eliciting the sentation of pain can be precisely measured in the trained observer and the physiological factors which raise or lower these thresholds can be experimentally determined, this is not the problem to be discussed here. Vague discomforts and nagging, but moderate, pains may be ignored. It is when the *meaning* of these discomforts or pains arouse fearful expectation that they may threaten emotional control. Pain and fear then pose the basic problem of emotion in medicine.

The meanings of pain and fear are not to be measured, as the physiologist is accustomed to do, in terms of controllable stimuli. No circumstance of the patient's daily living or of his past experience can be safely ignored. Even the most trivial experience or action, as mentioned earlier, is probably not what it seems. Recurrent guilty desires, impulses which the individual cannot resist or understand may menace his self-confidence and freedom of action. Almost by reflex action he may flinch or withdraw from familiar contacts because they arouse overpowering pain and fear.

In the previous discussion of Robert's case, the gravely threatening, though physically mild and harmless, electrical stimulation of his foreleg evoked vigorous and continuing attempts to escape from confinement at the beginning of training. However, in

34

the course of the first few experimental sessions Robert had imposed upon himself a degree of neuro-muscular restraint which permitted him to attempt only a token, symbolic escape pattern. At the signal intimating the approach of the theatening electric shock he attempted to escape from the demonstration box *by running away with one leg only.* His familiar and physically comfortable work place had become menacing and aroused in him the continuing pain and fear whose meaning we are now discussing.

His pain was not that aroused by stimulation of sensory nerve fibers but rather, pain in the sense of a painful memory or anticipation. The development during training of Robert's self-imposed restraint exacerbated the threat of the familiar experimental situation, thereby increasing the intensity of the pain and fear there aroused. The self-imposed re-straint originating during the course of conditioning, as we have described it, is in itself disabling.

In the case of the seeing-eye dog or the performing seal in the circus the self-imposed restraint developed through training *enhances* their effective and skilled behavior. Although they perform at signal, they do so with zest. Spontaneity and initiative are not quelled. Such animals are not brow-beaten. Freedom of action after the work period remains unimpaired. Not so with Robert. The disabling effects of his laboratory experience were reflected in his behavior as a "social" sheep in pasture, particularly with reference to his sexual behavior.

Robert's predicament, like that of our other condi-tioned animals, may be characterized as follows. The demonstration cabinet in which his conditioned responses are tested is a place of recurring threat to his safety. In consequence of our repeated menacing signals he is thrown into a state of continuing pain and fear ("anxiety"). This continuing pain and fear leads him to resort to endlessly repeated stereotyped, unsuccessful attempts to alleviate his anxious apprehension through escape. Because of his rigidly self-imposed restraint, he can only escape by symbolic and therefore ineffectual rhythmical flexions of one foreleg. These token escape movements are, however, inevitably followed by the dreaded, though harmless, shock.

The medical reference of the above discussion points to this question. How can man suffer the seemingly *unanimal* ills with which the psychiatrist has to deal? Our characterization of Robert's predicament seems not too unlike that of the psychoneurotic patient. Further comparison of disturbed animal and mental patient must be postponed for later discussion where the notion of man's "unanimal" mental ills will be explored.

For later medical reference, other emotional hazards encountered in conditioning can be identified and experimentally scrutinized: namely, loneliness, monotony, confusion and overstimulation. These four sinister threads are woven into the fabric of human living. They must be recognized and disentangled before we can decipher the hidden meanings of pain and fear.

Loneliness

The baleful influence of loneliness upon emotional control embraces the whole life span. Moreover, the individual's tolerance for the stress of isolation varies notably with age and temperament. An experimental analysis of loneliness must lead, then, to the basic problem of the nature of the social process. The lonely individual, since his avenues of communication have been blocked, becomes thereby an impoverished organism. These considerations suggest the importance of a broad biological approach to an understanding of the pervasive influence of loneliness upon mental health.

Deprivation of necessary social contact in the newborn and very young sheep or goat may disable the individual for life or may even prove lethal. Psychiatrists have observed the like in man. But since man can be lonely in emotionally more complex ways than other mammals, it will facilitate our analysis to begin with the simpler types of loneliness to be observed in sheep and goat. As compared with pig and dog, the sheep or goat engages in but few behavioral contacts which resemble what we should regard as emotional attachments. As an illustration of the validity of our assumption that there are no commonplaces of behavior, we proved to be mistaken in our earlier interpretation of the gregariousness of these grazing animals. It was our belief that sheep and goats grazed in flocks because they were compelled to satisfy a gregarious instinct and hence could not tolerate isolation. For this reason in our conditioned reflex laboratory we employed the services of a "social" sheep. It was tethered in a corner of the room where it could be seen at all times by the experimental sheep during the conditioning tests.

Preconceived ideas curtail freedom of experimentation and perseverance in observation. So it was in the present case and so it has been in numberless cases in the history of medical research. Experimental routine or laboratory habit too often continue of their own momentum and since our social sheep had become a laboratory fixture his presence went unchallenged. But the sheep is not necessarily lonely because it is alone, as further experimentation demonstrated.

When the social sheep was led from the room during the conditioning tests, the experimental sheep was not visibly perturbed. However, it exhibited a strong psychogalvanic response. This response was presumably an alerting reaction to a sudden visual alteration of its familiar environment since on the next day when its companion was absent, its deportment was calm and it reacted to the conditioned signals as before. It is, of course, obvious that words such as loneliness, companionship and gregariousness when used to characterize animal behavior are evaluative rather than descriptive. They are used to avoid circumlocution or the fabrication of technical terms to replace the words of common speech. The physician encounters the same difficulty in analyzing his patient's recital of symptoms.

We have no experimental evidence that the adult sheep or goat ever exhibits emotional evidences of loneliness when isolated from the flock. No differences can be observed between adults of either species conditioned when alone or whilst six or eight are being tested in the same room at the same time.

Each sheep or goat is a practicing solipsist and behaves within the confines of its private world. There are two exceptions: During the breeding season and during the period when the new mother must care for and suckle her young. The barrier of indifference to other members of the species then breaks down to be replaced by sexual excitement or maternal concern.

This analysis of gregariousness in the sheep and goat requires further comment. The gregarious behavior of a sheep or goat need not be limited to members of its own species. Twenty years ago Dr. and Mrs. Quinn Curtis in our Behavior Farm Laboratory adopted a female lamb a few days of age and raised it on a bottle. This sheep (named "Aida" because of her vocal powers as a lamb) lived for five years without contact with other sheep. As a lamb she depended upon Mrs. Curtis for food and the "flock" of which she was a member included a three year old girl, a cocker spaniel and a German shepherd. Aida played with the little girl and the dogs and rode in the family automobile. She was observed to chase strange dogs from the yard and to contest with her dog companions for their food. At five years of age, when confined alone in a paddock, she waded in tall fresh grass without grazing. Her favorite foods remained dog biscuit and bread crusts until her death at five years. Such instances are not uncommon. Many farm children make pets of lambs, kids, or little pigs. The goat in harness pulling the children's cart used to be a familiar sight.

In discussing the biological basis of psychic trauma, evidence has already been given for the disabling effects of subjecting the lamb or kid to the stresses of conditioning when isolated from its mother. In both sheep and goat from one month of age on, the stress of training does not seem to be alleviated by the presence of the mother, of any other member of the species, or of the experimenter himself.

Monotony

Upon the background of the experimental animal's rigidly self-imposed restraint the stresses characteristic of the classical conditioning procedures include monotony, confusion, and overstimulation. Each of these procedures employed alone or in combination inevitably leads to continuing pain and fear—to experimental neurosis. Sometimes the onset of the chronic emotional disorder occurs with dramatic suddenness but more often so insidiously that the observer may fail to note its prodromal signs.

The inflexible reiteration of alarms when long continued cannot be well tolerated either by man or animal. Regularly recurring crises, even if only nuisances, impose upon the individual a pattern of waxing and waning stress whose cumulative effect may be injurious.

A familiar example of the disturbing effects of a recurring nuisance is the ringing of the telephone. When one is alone at home and his privacy is repeatedly invaded by the telephone bell, though he has decided in advance to ignore it, the experience becomes increasingly unpleasant and disturbing.

Had we continued our earlier demonstration and subjected Robert to the ringing of the door bell for 10 seconds every minute, even though he did not answer by flexing his foreleg, his excitement as revealed by restlessness, disturbed and rapid breathing, teeth grinding, would be observed to mount steadily. In fact, the enforced monotony of regularly repeated no-shock signals has precipitated experimental neuroses in a number of our sheep.

The choice of mammals as simple as the sheep and goat has proved fortunate for our purpose in seeking to specify the environmental conditions adversely affecting emotional control. For example, it is possible in the sheep and goat to disentangle the emotional hazards of loneliness and monotony. In individuals more than a month of age isolation during conditioning does not elicit the emotional manifestations of loneliness to be observed in the dog, who does not wish to be separated from his master during testing.

Two simple experiments will demonstrate the complex dynamics of the sheep's reaction to a rigid time schedule of conditioned signals imposed upon it day after day. The sheep confined within the testing cabinet for an hour each day received the usual mild electric shock to its foreleg every 6 minutes but *without warning signal*. Its expectation of the shock can be based only upon the passage of time from one shock to the next. However, in the course of a few days it gives evidence of having become conditioned to the 6 minute pauses between shocks but its estimate of the passage of time is quite inexact. One or two minutes before the shock is due it exhibits restlessness with small tentative and irregular flexions of the foreleg accompanied by increased respiration and cardiac acceleration. Sometimes it is caught unawares by the shock. However, such failures to respond probably represent inaccurate estimation of time since if shock is occasionally omitted when it falls due, the sheep may give its anticipatory reaction a minute or two after the instant when the shock should have been given.

In our experience sheep subjected to this monotonous regimen of forced reaction to shock without warning, every 6 minutes, do not lose emotional control. They can tolerate the stresses imposed by this simple type of monotonous training.

With these same animals, however, another slightly different procedure inevitably leads to chronic emotional disorder. Every 6 minutes a 10 second signal precedes the shock. Now, the sheep maintains its pose of quiet alertness and does not become restless as the end of the 6 minute period of waiting draws to a close. When the signal is given, however, it instantly raises its head, pricks up its ears, then crouches and executes the unhurried flexions of the foreleg with the same stereotyped precision which we observed in Robert's case. Later, the invariable sequence of changes in this sheep's behavior which precede its emotional breakdown (or experimental neurosis) will be described. At this time it will suffice to mention the *experimenter's* emotional reaction to this training regimen when he subjects himself to the same stressful monotony.

If the experimenter elects to keep time and to administer the signals and shocks by pressing the appropriate keys, he will shortly become acutely aware of the almost intolerable discomfort of keeping time along with the sheep undergoing its daily hour-long test.

The duration of the period of waiting between signals is of crucial importance in determining the degree of stress exerted upon the animal by the repetition of these signals.

At the beginning of the experiments on the influence of monotony on emotional control we supposed that conflict took precedence over monotony as the precipitating factor in the onset of experimental neurosis. In these earlier experiments the sheep was subjected to the alternation of positive and negative signals spaced seven minutes apart, repeated for an hour each day. The result of continuing this procedure day after day was inevitably the onset of experimental neurosis.

We assumed, therefore, that conflict was engendered and perpetuated by the rhythmical recurrence of these signals of opposite meaning when evenly spaced in time. The monotony of the rigid time schedule was regarded as of secondary importance in leading to loss of emotional control. Our assumption was invalid as the following simple experiment demonstrated.

Instead, of alternating positive and negative signals at seven minute intervals, positive signals alone were repeated every 7 minutes during the daily test hour. Thus, instead of conflict plus monotony, the animal was here subjected to the emotional hazard of monotony alone. Yet the onset of neurosis was in nowise influenced. The absence of conflict between positive and negative signals failed either to alter the length of training necessary to precipitate the emotional crisis or to affect its chronicity when it appeared.

The experimental factor crucial in determining the degree of stress to which the sheep (or goat) was subjected by the monotonous reiteration of positive signals always followed by shock proved to be the number of minutes elapsing between signals. *Stress increases as the interval of waiting between signals increases.* In experiments extending over the past twenty-five years we have tested the effect of constant intervals of waiting varying from one to seven minutes where the standard test period was one hour. Paradoxically, during this hour the longer the constant periods of waiting and, consequently, the *fewer the signals warning of shock,* the greater the stress which the animal must endure.

Confusion

Self-imposed restraint, loneliness, monotony, confusion, and overstimulation are always operating in diverse and subtle combinations to influence adversely the maintenance of emotional control in ourselves. The experimental analysis of their separate influences in concrete instances of human and animal behavior must be pursued in order to gain further understanding of the basic social process common to mammals.

This basic social process is anchored in self-imposed restraint. Its simplest and most easily controlled manifestation is the self-imposed restraint to be observed as it develops during conditioning as we have described it. Its most subtle and complex manifestations are found in what John Whitehorn identifies as obligatory patterns of living. A person who follows such a pattern is one who willingly, or of necessity, assumes certain obligations to other individuals or groups, or attempts to live according to certain religious precepts. These precepts may be formalized or not, depending upon the individual's education and temperament.

In the wild state deer may flee in panic if they detect the scent of man borne to them on a wind capriciously shifting direction. Becoming confused in estimating the position of the hunter, they flee and in so doing terminate their panic. On the other hand, the conditioned animal during the daily test can neither escape, nor otherwise master its uncertainty as to what impends.

A drastic experimental maneuver for inducing confusion in the conditioned animal was first introduced by Pavlov. A dog with a stable organization of expectancies, positive and negative, with respect to the prospects of being fed was subjected to the following test. Suppose that through many months of conditioning the metronome clicking at 60 per minute intimated the coming of food. Other signals indicating food were a door buzzer, an electric light, and the rhythmical but light stimulation of a shaved spot on the thigh. Negative signals indicating no food to follow included the metronome at 120 per minute, a door bell, and the rhythmical tactile stimualtion of a spot on the chest.

This unsuspecting dog who believes his laboratory world to be a place where he can safely depend upon what is to happen next comes to his work place one day and is rudely deceived. All familiar signals now mean the opposite. Food appears only following metronome 120, door bell and tactile stimulation of the spot on his chest.

In our own experience the dog is an earnest seeker

after certainty in his circumscribed laboratory world. Even the white rat, gentled from birth, becomes surly and even vicious when confusion replaces certainty of anticipation in its laboratory tests.

In Pavlov's dramatic experiments the temperament of the dog seemed to be the principal determining factor in the emotional outcome when his world was suddenly turned upside down. The dogs who adjusted promptly to the new order inaugurated by reversal of signals had inherited what he described as a labile nervous system. The other emotionally more rigid dogs lost emotional control and became experimentally neurotic.

But novelty does not necessarily involve confusion. The unexpected can give the tingle of adventure. However, the dog faced with a reversal of all familiar signals was, through its self-imposed restraint, incapable of ignoring the puzzling change-about of these signals. It was, through this long established habit of holding itself in, incapable of resorting to exploratory activity or other avenues for achieving emotional let-down.

A less spectacular method for subjecting the conditioned animal to the emotional hazard of confusion was demonstrated in Robert's case. In the early period of training positive and negative signals are chosen by the experimenter which can be easily and clearly discriminated by the animal; for example, metronome at 60 beats per minute followed by shock, as contrasted with metronome at 120 per minute never resulting in shock to the foreleg. Here, the onset of confusion is insidious. Only very gradually, over months of training, does the rapid negative rate slow down until it

is confusingly similar to the positive metronome rate
of 60 per minute. In Robert's case it will be remembered that the progressive slowing of the negative
metronome proceeded stepwise. Thus, metronome
120 per minute was reduced to 100, 92, 84, 78 and
finally 72 per minute.

As this regimen of gradually "closing in" is adhered
to week after week, the animal becomes unremittingly
and increasingly puzzled in its laboratory environment. Its emotional control now balances precari-
ously on the razor edge of painful apprehension. The
subtle, almost insensible changes in its deportment
from day to day foretell the emotional breakdown or
experimental neurosis inevitably to follow.

Overstimulation

In the analysis of the effects of overstimulation on
the emotional control of our animals we have refrained from the use of such excessively intense
stimuli as "blinding light," "deafening noise," or
sudden and unbearably painful stimulation of the
body as in burns, lacerations, or fractures. The
soldier in the combat situation is trained to maintain
some measure of emotional control in such emergen-
cies. Moreover, he is provided with the social and
medical resources necessary to aid him in counter-
balancing their emotional impact. The ethics of experimentation in the field of animal behavior do not
sanction this type of study. Imposing physical distress upon the helpless animal could make no con-
tribution to the physician's knowledge that would
enable him more successfully to alleviate his patient's
pain and fear. Our research goals, as students of ani-

mal behavior, are all positive and focus on the problems of *preventive* psychiatry.

"Biting off more than you can chew" is the usual kind of overstimulation that leads to emotional disaster in everyday life. A simpler but similar situation can be demonstrated to obtain in the case of our sheep and goats. The conditioned sheep trapped by its self-imposed restraint must perforce accept the task which the experimenter assigns it for the daily test and may thus be forced to bite off more than it can chew.

The first experimental neurosis observed in our laboratory in 1927 was the accidental, and quite unexpected, result of the experimenter's impetuosity in trying to force a conditioned sheep to yield data more rapidly for a scientific report being prepared to meet an approaching deadline.

The original conditioning schedule before the speed-up consisted of ten metronome signals per day each followed by shock and spaced one to three minutes apart. This daily task remained constant for some weeks. But then the number of signals was increased to fifteen on one day and further increased to twenty on the following day. The conditioned stimulus load thus increased abruptly and within three days had been doubled. There was no crowding of the signals, however, since they were still spaced one to three minutes apart.

The sheep was unable to adjust emotionally to this new load and suddenly within the span of a day lost its self-imposed restraint. It could no longer contain its excitement but executed repeated, vigorous flexions of the trained foreleg. Its reactions to the metronome signals now consisted of very rapid and violent flexions of this limb with much squirming in the restraining harness.

On ensuing days when prepared for the familiar tests, its agitation as indicated by repeated head and ear movements together with violent, spontaneous flexions of the foreleg, continued in the absence of all signals. Moreover, in contrast to its former docility, it resisted being led to the laboratory and its cardiac perturbation could be demonstrated in the barn at night. Despite long vacations in the pasture its chronic emotional disorder endured until death at thirteen-and-a-half years.

Although basically similar from a biological point of view, the case of our overstimulated sheep and a child forced to bite off more than he can chew differ importantly in the influences operating to effect such overstimulation. The child (or adult in the appropriate situation) goaded to performance beyond his capacity is reacting to socially complex pressures not operating in the lives of our simple farm animals. The results, however, may be as emotionally disabling in the one case as in the other. When the parent's or teacher's level of aspiration is foisted upon the child, he enters upon a regimen of living in home or school where emotional hazards abound and where the probability of emotional crippling rapidly increases. This, however, is not the place to attempt to document such a statement.

In the previous discussion detailing the vicissitudes of daily living which threaten emotional control in animal and man a gloomy prospect was depicted. On the other hand, it was stated that the goals of the investigator of animal behavior are *positive* and aim at the furtherance of mental health by contributing to the understanding of emotional control.

The medical student learns to recognize an alarming array of obscure organ dysfunctions only to discover when he becomes a practicing physician that patients come to him in a state of pain and fear. This presenting emotional problem must be attacked by penetrating to the *meaning* of the patient's pain and fear in order that appetite and zest may be restored to him. In this sense every physician, regardless of the gravity of organ dysfunction or other disability which he may discover, must be a *preventive psychiatrist*.

An anatomist plus a physiologist plus a pathologist plus a bacteriologist plus a biochemist does not make a physician. The modern doctor in addition to his formidable equipment of laboratory and diagnostic skills must develop the sensitivities of naturalist and sociologist in observing the nuances of ordinary human behavior. He can never ignore the fact that man is both *idealist* and *animal*. In this incongruity of roles is to be discovered the fundamental meaning of human pain and fear.

Chapter IV

Neurotic Behavior

THE ATTEMPT to understand emotional disorders responsible for the inability of psychoneurotic patients and experimentally neurotic animals to cope with real life situations as they occur poses the same basic problem for psychiatrist and behaviorist. If the behavior of an individual, patient, or animal, seems to the investigator strange and unaccountable, he must perseveringly explore the life history of that individual until his strange or ever irrational actions become natural and understandable.

Ernest Jones says of Freud's characteristic way of working: "His great strength, though sometimes also his weakness, was the quite extraordinary respect he had for the *singular fact*. This is surely a very rare quality. In scientific work people continually dismiss a single observation when it does not appear to have any connection with other data or general knowledge. Not so Freud. The single fact would fascinate him and he could not dismiss it from his mind until he had found some explanation of it. The practical value of this mental quality depends on another one: judgment. The fact in question may really be insignificant and the explanation of it of no interest: that way lies crankiness. But it may be a previously hidden jewel or a speck of gold that indicates a vein of ore. Psychology cannot yet explain on what the flair or intuition depends that guides the observer to follow up something his feelings tell him is important, not as a thing in itself but as an example of some wide law of nature."

A strong suspicion arises, however, that this flair or intuition is for the most part the result of dispassionate and persevering observation; in other words, long continued hard work.

Before turning to a discussion of the implications for mental medicine of experimental neurosis it will be useful to review some *singular facts* which have been noted from time to time in the course of our studies of sheep and goat behavior. Each of these singular facts would have seemed to the casual observer strange, unaccountable, even irrational. But when reviewed in relation to the individual's known life history, they become understandable and reasonable. They then take their proper place in the animal's contemporary emotional organization.

On one occasion the animal attendant at the laboratory came to us to report a disturbing experience. When he went to the barn to feed the animals, one of his favorite goats fled in alarm at his approach. It would not come to him even when offered a bucket of oats although they had been on friendly terms since it was a kid. He feared that we might suspect him of mistreating the animals. Actually, we had learned to trust his practical knowledge of farm animals. Their well-being was his principal concern.

Although this attendant regularly assisted us in preparing our sheep and goats for their daily training sessions, he did not really know what we were up to. He only knew that ordinarily the animals came willingly to the laboratory and that they were not mistreated by punishment or rough handling. What he did not know was that his friend, the goat, had reached a stage in its stressful conditioning in which it had begun to carry its troubles back to the barn. Fleeing from the familiar attendant was a clear indication to us that this goat's anxious apprehension had spread from its place of origin in the laboratory to its living quarters. It was already flinching or withdrawing from its familiar environmental contacts and was entering upon a state of continuing pain and fear; namely, a chronic loss of emotional control or experimental neurosis. Thus, the singular fact of the goat's irrational fear of the friendly attendant was for us an important datum in analyzing its case history.

Another singular fact was noted by this same attendant, who regularly reported cases of sickness in the flock. In mid morning of a pleasant summer day he entered the barn through the doors which had been left open and found a solitary lamb three months of age lying on its side. The other sheep were in the pasture. He at once reported a sick lamb in the barn but when he returned, it had already joined the flock. This lamb, just before it was found lying in the barn, had been released from the laboratory at the end of its daily conditioning test. It was the same castrate male lamb, mentioned in the previous chapter, which was being subjected to our twenty darkness signal stress routine in the absence of its mother. When it was observed lying alone in the barn, it had already begun to exhibit profound lethargy and almost complete inertness upon stimulation during the experimental hour. Shortly after entering the laboratory room it lay down with head pressed to the floor.

At the dimming of the lights for ten seconds it, typically, gave no observable response and rolled but slightly to the side at the shock which followed. Moreover, this was the twin lamb which, as already related, had recently given up following his mother and twin brother as she was led to the laboratory with the normal brother following. It will be remembered, also, that this was the same lamb that died at ten months while its "protected" twin attained healthy maturity. This lethargy and solitariness in a lamb so young when on its own outside the laboratory was certainly a singular fact.

Reviewing the three decades of our uninterrupted observations on conditioning and experimental neurosis in sheep and goat has brought to light a number of disturbing considerations. Perhaps the most serious handicap to the progress of our work in years gone by was a *quantitative delusion*. We were too often preoccupied with the measurement of stimuli to the neglect of the *meaning of these stimuli* for the individual animal.

If a motor nerve is stimulated electrically, its muscle contracts and the strength of the stimulus in relation to the magnitude of the contraction is precisely measurable. It will be remembered that this was not so in Robert's case. An electric current barely perceptible to us elicited a vigorous withdrawal of his foreleg. This brief and feeble electric current meant danger and, because of his previous experiences, so did the metronome clicking once a second and the sounding of the door buzzer. Fast and slow metronome rates, bell and buzzer could be called conditioned stimuli, thus suggesting the primary importance of measuring them as exactly as possible. Their significance for Robert, however, was that they were questions to which he knew the answers. When one of these signals was given, he knew what to expect and acted accordingly.

Although we do not underestimate the importance of careful graphic recording and measuring of conditioned responses, our often overly elaborate instrumentation caused us to lose sight of our animal in a thicket of levers, cables, wires, recording pens and reams of kymograph paper. We have kept as a souvenir of those days a kymograph record of a goat's conditioned reflexes. During an interval between signals the respiratory tracing shows a puzzling series of violent and rapid excursions of the recording pen. The goat was only scratching his ribs with his horn.

Another handicap to the progress of our work has been that the investigator was inclined to become laboratory-centered both in his observing and thinking. In that cloistered atmosphere with his familiar tools at hand he saw his animal subjects come and go. When they left the laboratory at the end of a session with their behavior therein duly recorded, the temptation was great to adopt the attitude of "out of sight, out of mind." The psychiatrist with a full schedule of appointments for his working hours can become similarly cloistered in his consulting room. It is a mental hazard shared, at least to some degree, by behaviorist and psychiatrist.

Now this laboratory-centered habit of thinking has perhaps in the past led us unwittingly to misrepresent the nature of the experimental neurosis. The impression was somehow conveyed to psychiatrists that the experimental neurosis in animals was a laboratory artifact or trick. Quite "artificial" behavior was produced; somewhat like teaching a horse to count. Hence, it was believed that neurotic behavior in animals could have little or no relevance for everyday emotional problems or psychoneurotic disturbances.

This misapprehension of the nature of experimental neurosis has resulted from confusing two questions. First, what are the symptoms of the animal's lack of emotional control? Then, what specific procedures were employed in the laboratory to precipitate this chronic emotional disability? It was reasoned that since the specific symptoms originated from stresses imposed upon the animal during its laboratory tests, that these symptoms must be found in the situation of their origin, namely, the laboratory. Therefore, bringing the animal to the laboratory, or seeing its trainer outside the laboratory, or anything specifically reminding it of its experiences in the laboratory will elicit the appropriate symptoms of alarm. Otherwise its behavior will be normal.

This is wrong. Our neurotic animals' chronic emotional disturbance is self-perpetuating. It lives a life of its own and reveals itself in whatever situation the animal finds itself: pasture, barn, laboratory, or lecture hall. In any of these situations the seemingly normal sheep or goat will exhibit, upon occasion, easily overlooked eccentricities of behavior indicating that all is not well in its emotional world.

For example, the animal with most experience in conditioning at the Behavior Farm Laboratory is the goat, "Brown Billy," now in his ninth year. His responses are so precise and dependable that we have used him for several years to demonstrate conditioned reflexes to psychiatrists and psychologists. His deportment in lecture hall, laboratory, or barnyard is at all times dignified and venerable. Quite by accident, however, we discovered that he was a very worried animal. A new electric fence had been installed in the barnyard. One of my colleagues glancing out of the laboratory window saw Brown Billy approach the unfamiliar strand of wire. He hesitantly touched the wire with his muzzle and instantly wheeled and dashed away. But then he suddenly stopped, wheeled to face the wire and precisely flexed his *right* foreleg.

This peculiar and, indeed, unrealistic reaction to a situation of danger would puzzle a casual observer. What purpose was served in facing the electrified wire and so precisely flexing his foreleg after the shock on the muzzle had already been experienced? No other peculiarities of behavior had been noted which would set him apart from the other goats in our flock. As previously mentioned, when a person behaves in what seems to us a peculiar manner, his conduct often becomes familiar and reasonable when we learn more of his past and particularly of certain significant emotional problems that he has faced. This is common sense psychology and makes life happier for all of us. Our knowledge of Brown Billy's previous emotional experiences in the laboratory enables us to understand his peculiar behavior in the barnyard.

He had been trained in the laboratory for several months according to the following schedule. For an hour each day, while confined by a restraining harness and with electrodes attached to the right foreleg, a buzzer was sounded for 10 seconds, followed immediately by a mild electric shock to this limb. Forty of these buzzer signals, spaced a minute apart, were given at each session.

If the goat kept his foreleg flexed until the buzzer stopped, he received no shock. After a few days he caught on and always flexed his foreleg at the buzzer and kept it flexed until the sound ceased. Although he had not received a shock for several weeks, his prompt and precise flexion at the sound of the buzzer continued without lapse. Now, in the barnyard, the novel experience of electric shock on the muzzle promptly released the inappropriate behavior of running from the fence, wheeling, and *then* making the avoidance response.

During the past two years further observations indicate that this goat has developed a definite and chronic emotional disorder (which is all that Pavlov meant by his unhappy term, experimental neurosis). As illustrated by his bizarre behavior toward the electric fence, the pattern of Brown Billy's emergency reaction to danger has become *highly simplified and stereotyped*. We no longer apply shocks to his foreleg no matter what he does during the test period, and although the buzzer signal has now been repeated more than 2,000 times, the goat still continues to maintain flexion of his right foreleg as long as the buzzer is sounding. He will not, or cannot, take a chance. He has become a perfectionist and always does just the right thing when menaced by the buzzer. However, his perfectionism now amounts to mental illness. All sudden stimuli such as turning on bright lights, starting a movie camera, tapping his side lightly with a wooden rod instantly evoke a brisk and maintained flexion. All alarms are now channelled through his right foreleg.

What keeps this simple and stereotyped response going when there is no longer anything in Brown Billy's real situation to be avoided? Is not this fundamentally the same question which the psychiatrist faces in combatting his neurotic patient's phobias? There seems to be no reason why the operation of painful or "traumatic" memories may not be inferred in both cases.

In attempting to understand these chronic emotional incapacities in our neurotic sheep and goats *originating situations* must take precedence over *resulting symptoms.*

Because of man's incredibly complicated cognitive machinery, his neurotic symptoms may exhibit a bewildering diversity. Nevertheless, our emotionally disturbed animals under careful observation show many of the same or closely similar symptoms. The physician is in a much better position, however, to explore and analyze his psychoneurotic patient's symptomology than is the behaviorist in the case of his experimentally neurotic animal. When it comes to analyzing the *originating situations,* responsible for chronic loss of emotional control, the shoe is on the other foot. The behaviorist can *create and rigorously control* the situations in which experimental neuroses originate. Moreover, these laboratory situations can be *exactly recreated* by other investigators.

For the sheep or goat its laboratory room becomes, through daily association, just a corner of the pasture. This familiar room is then a small part of the animal's total living space. The scheduled test hour, likewise, can become just as specific and familiar a portion of its daily round of activities as milking time is for the cow. When time and place for conditioning thus become an accepted part of the sheep or goat's daily experience, there is no reason for regarding the atmosphere of the laboratory as in any sense artificial. The experimental animal's behavior therein is just as "natural" as its behavior whilst loitering in the barnyard or grazing in pasture.

The essential difference, however, between its loitering in the barnyard and its deportment during the conditioning tests is this. As the animal enters the laboratory room and takes its station in the restraining harness, its habitual self-imposed restraint forces it to submit to the "rules and regulations" of the testing hour. These rules and regulations consist in the conditioning procedures which the experimenter elects to employ. The animal does not rebel against these familiar rules and regulations because, through training, it has relinquished its freedom of action and, for the hour, becomes a passive agent responding to the experimenter's signals as best it can.

Lenin was enthusiastic about Pavlov's work—so much so that he caused continued support of Pavlov's laboratories to be written into Soviet law. There is reason to believe that his enthusiasm was based upon practical considerations. Animal conditioning offered him a key to social control. It pointed the way to achieving passive acceptance of social, economic and political "rules and regulations" by the masses. Later on, we shall pursue some leads from investigations of animal behavior indicating possible ways in which such attitudes of fatalism and passive acceptance may be combatted.

For the present, however, let us follow the course of a typical experimental neurosis in the sheep from the place and circumstances of its origin. In this way we shall discover how the onset of such an emotional crisis and its perseveration will distort the animal's subsequent pattern of living and will disable it in its attempts to master successfully the critical situations it may later encounter.

In our laboratory seven doors lead from the barnyard into adjoining experimental rooms, each ten feet square. For the experiment now to be described two of these rooms A and B, were provided with identical equipment for conditioning. A sheep six months old was brought daily to room A for simple conditioning to the sound of the door buzzer always followed by shock to the foreleg. With a schedule of ten buzzer signals per day irregularly spaced over the test hour, training was continued to include one hundred repetitions of the buzzer each followed by the usual brief, mild shock. As in Robert's case, this sheep's response to the sound of the buzzer shortly assumed the usual pattern of precise and unhurried flexions of the foreleg.

It has often happened in the course of our work that an attempt to demonstrate to students what we think we know about the animal's behavior has resulted in the animal teaching us, thereby revealing a new lead to further investigation. That is what transpired in the present case. The sheep under discussion had been briefly conditioned to the buzzer in prepara-

tion for a demonstration to students of what happens
during the extinction of a conditioned reflex.

On the day of the demonstration our sheep was
led into the unfamiliar room B, next door to A, where
her preparatory training had taken place. The demonstration then proceeded as follows. The buzzer was
sounded and the sheep gave her usual precise response
followed by brisk withdrawal of the foreleg at the
shock. After a minute the buzzer again elicited the
conditioned response terminated as always by shock.
Now after a pause of three minutes we were prepared to demonstrate the extinction of a conditioned
reflex. The sheep meanwhile was not distracted by the
students' presence since they were viewing her
through a window.

Since the sounds of door bell and door buzzer are
somewhat similar, experience had shown us that the
sheep would doubtless respond to the bell as she did
to the familiar buzzer, thus demonstrating the phenomenon of generalization of the conditioned reflex.
So, in order to bring about extinction, we chose to
sound the door bell for ten seconds every minute.
When the sheep no longer flexed her leg at the bell,
extinction would be complete. However, our demonstration proved a signal failure.

At the first sound of the bell our ewe, as we had
predicted, gave the same precise conditioned response
as she had to the buzzer just three minutes before.
Now, as the bell continued, for 10 seconds every minute, the repeated flexions of her foreleg at this sound
gradually diminished in number and amplitude with
increasing sluggishness of response. So far so good.
But beginning with the twentieth repetition of the

door bell the frequency and vigor of these movements began increasing and by the thirtieth bell the sheep was visibly disturbed. Meanwhile, numerous small tic-like movements of her foreleg were noted during the pauses between signals. These characteristic nervous movements, as we knew from previous experience, clearly indicated that an experimental neurosis had been precipitated.

On the next day the sheep was brought again to room B and the previous schedule repeated. Her agitation was now intense, with frequent and vigorous flexion of the foreleg not only in response both to bell and buzzer but every few seconds during the pauses between signals. Our sheep was now manifesting the signs of a full-blown experimental neurosis of the agitated type. These signs included constant head and ear movements, frequent shifts of posture, sudden starts as if in response to a loud noise, frequent and seemingly involuntary movements of the trained foreleg (as just mentioned), labored breathing, rapid irregular pulse, together with frequent micturition and defecation. This agitated type of experimental neurosis is common in sheep subjected to the stress of conditioning and its signs were quite familiar to us. Moreover, in such cases the onset of the animal's uncontrolled agitation occurs with dramatic suddenness.

Our demonstration which was intended to illustrate the phenomenon of extinction but turned into a demonstration of the onset of experimental neurosis had an important outcome, largely the result of accident. It had usually been our practice to continue the conditioning of a sheep or goat in the same laboratory room from start to finish. In the present instance, however, we were fortunate in having carried through the brief preliminary conditioning of our demonstration sheep in room A while its emotional breakdown occurred soon thereafter in room B next door. What would happen if this very recently neurotic sheep were returned to room A where all had gone well?

To answer this question the following experiment was performed. With her manifest neurosis but two days old, our demonstration sheep was brought to room B, placed in the restraining harness with recording apparatus adjusted as before, but no signals or shocks were given. Her extreme agitation continued for fifteen minutes. She was the released, led into the barnyard and then at once into room A. Once more with recording apparatus adjusted, she was allowed to stand in the restraining harness without signals or shocks for another fifteen minute period. During this time her behavior was normal in every observable respect. Her pose was quiet but alert, with little or no head movement, breathing was slow and regular, and there was no fidgeting with the trained foreleg or other manifestations of nervousness. *At this stage her neurotic symptoms were strictly limited to the situation of their origin in room B.* In room A she resumed her status of normal sheep.

Now on each day she was allowed to stand for fifteen minutes in the restraining harness without signals or shocks, first in one room then the other. Whether she was taken first into room A or room B was left to chance. *But within three days of the beginning of this routine without signals or shocks she was as agitated in room A as in room B.* Room A was no longer a safe place. Her neurotic symptoms had now broken free from their place of origin in room B.

Our animals, in which loss of emotional control is chronic, will exhibit the characteristic signs of their experimental neurosis in any laboratory room in the building. We had never before caught the neurosis at its place of origin and timed its spread to embrace the rest of the animal's daily environment.

To trace the life course of the neurotic process further, let us imagine a *composite sheep* whose eccentricities and symptoms include all the neurotic sheep we have known.

If our composite sheep is with the flock clustered closely together in the barnyard, he will give himself away if we casually stroll toward the flock. As we approach, the flock will shortly take alarm and dash away. The neurotic sheep, on the other hand, will run in the opposite direction all by himself. When dogs get into the pasture, it is always this composite sheep which we later find dead from its injuries.

Furthermore, the neurotic sheep gives evidence of continuing in a state of anxious apprehension both by night and by day. Since sheep do not sleep as soundly as dogs, pigs, or men, it would be inappropriate to speak of the neurotic sheep as a sufferer from insomnia. If the sheep's movements are registered from a recording platform in the barnyard, the normal animal will be found to be resting quietly at night. Our composite sheep, on the other hand, is "walking the floor" all night long and continues his restless pacing during the day as well.

Another evidence of the neurotic animal's continuing alarm during the night appears if we examine its heart rate without its knowledge. This is most simply accomplished by means of a long distance stethoscope —a long thick-walled rubber tube leading from the animal's chest to a listening post outside of the barn where the flock is resting. In contrast to the normal sheep's slow, steady heart beat during the night, the disturbed animal's heart rate is rapid and variable responding by sudden acceleration to slight sounds which have no effect on the steady heart rate of the normal sheep.

As old age approaches, our composite sheep's neurosis does not abate. He is a life-long neurotic. Vacations at pasture for as long as three years bring only temporary improvement. When he returns to the laboratory and resumes his conditioning routine, the neurotic manifestations exhibited there are soon as prominent as before. Moreover, change of scene is of no benefit. He brings his neurosis with him to a new farm and a new laboratory.

Among the disturbing considerations which a review of our previous work has brought to light the most disturbing has been saved until the last. *How do we know when a sheep or goat has become experimentally neurotic?*

Our composite sheep, whose life-long neurotic disabilities we have been describing, is a synthetic product of those animals in which the experimental neurosis appeared with dramatic suddenness as uncontrollable agitation in the familiar laboratory environment. However, such clear-cut cases of severe experimental neurosis only point the way to a much more difficult field of investigation.

During the past ten years we have become convinced that all conditioning procedures which are based upon the animal's self-imposed restraint will, if long enough continued, cause that animal to become experimentally neurotic. When does the neurosis begin and by what signs may we first detect it?

Our sheep, Robert, and our goat, Brown Billy, were long considered to be highly skilled in their conditioned behavior and completely normal animals. It was only by accident that we became aware of Robert's sexual disturbance and it was by chance, also, that Brown Billy's eccentric behavior at his first contact with the new electric fence was noted.

In the discussion of stress and emotion to follow we shall review some of the more subtle changes in the conditioned animal's behavior indicating the insidious onset of neurotic incapacity.

Addendum to Chapter IV

Some Observations on the Training of Horses

By

FRANCES H. PROCHAZKA[*]

THE FOLLOWING account is by way of setting down a few personal observations of the effect upon horses when their training is hurried.

The young animals (about 3 years, since the breeds we work with are slow to mature) are given a certain training program to fit them either to be ridden or to be driven, or both. There are certain usages and signals to which they must become accustomed and to which they must respond if they are to be safe and pleasant to use. The animal is usually given a half to one-hour handling period daily, followed by a one-hour training period on six days of the week. This program is continued over a period of some months depending upon the degree to which the training is carried. The necessary fundamentals require two months—providing the animal is tractable and of average intelligence—and include: standing quietly on signal or command, walking forward on signal or command, acceptance of saddle, bridle, and harness,

---

[*] Mrs. Frances Prochazka (Airy Acres Farm, Box 34, Etna, N.Y.) a former student in our laboratory, has kindly permitted us to present her observations based upon more than twelve years experience in training horses.

carrying or pulling weight, turning to right or left respectively in response to signal of right and left rein, specific responses to signals of body weight and leg pressure for stopping, moving forward, and turning either to right or left. Command is understood as being a spoken word; signal, as any other non-verbal indication—i.e. shifting body weight, pressure of leg, rein, heel, whip, or spur. The handling period is used to accustom the animal to the trainer, to establish confidence and mutual rapport. A large part of it is spent in teaching the animal to accept all sorts of normally frightening objects, such as paper bags, flapping rags, loud noises, sudden movements, etc. The handling and training periods are given ideally at the same hour every day and at the same place. The trainer uses the animal's natural movements and inclinations toward movement as a starting point, modifies gradually toward the desired response, rewards any indication of the desired response by edible tidbits, stroking, vocal murmurs of approval, then repeats and repeats the sequence until the desired response becomes stable—and then starts all over again to establish a new or a more elaborate response. The trainer endeavors to avoid any reinforcement that is painful or frightening to the animal, although this may occasionally be necessary. It is also most important that the trainer keep the animal's interest and attention focused on the task at hand if learning is to proceed satisfactorily. This necessitates some ingenuity so that the necessary repetitions do not become boring.

I have observed two ways in which an animal can be hurried. Each individual animal seems to have a

natural pace or rhythm of movement which soon becomes obvious to the experienced trainer. One cannot push this individual movement rate very much
without the animal becoming irritable and somewhat
unresponsive. Depending on individual temperament,
the animal may become nervous, jerky, and erratic
or slow, balky, and lethargic. These effects are most
noticeable when the pace is set too fast for the animal.
However, there is some effect—generally toward
habitual lethargy—when the pace is held too slow.
The more obvious way in which the animal may be
hurried is to attempt to speed up the learning process
beyond the capability to establish stable responses.
This can be done in a variety of ways—by giving a new
sequence before an older one is firmly established, by
trying to establish three or four responses simultaneously (two, if chosen carefully, can be handled at
once) giving signals too close in time for the animal
to give a full response, failure to systematically review
previously established responses, substantially length-
ening the daily training period, and other variations
in a similar vein. In Dr. Liddell's terms, the animal is
being confused and overstimulated in such cases. In
my observation, all cases of this kind of hurrying result in a degree of failure or complete failure to establish stable responses, along with a marked disintegra-
tion of the animal's disposition. The individual may
become excessively and inappropriately active or
lethargic, and shows ill-temper—i.e. laying back of
ears, biting, nipping, kicking, or intention-movements
of same.

   These effects have never been systematically pushed
into extreme cases since we are interested in produc-

ing reliable, pleasant, and useful animals; however, some mistakes have been made, and I shall cite two partial case histories as examples of the forementioned dispositional effects.

Laddie was the first horse I taught to jump—to leap over obstacles while traveling forward at a fairly rapid pace and carrying a rider. To make a long story short, he was presented with too many jumps, jumps that were too high or raised in height too rapidly, too great a variety of jumps—all in too short a time. The training program was good—the same given successfully to other animals—except that this initial attempt was given too rapidly. It was not a success. Indeed, the adverse effects of extreme nervous agitation when brought to a jumping field—nervous biting, pawing, kicking, and tail switching, dancing about, fighting restraint of bit and reins, greatly increased respiration and heartbeat, along with profuse sweating—numerous refusals to jump and absolute refusal in Horse-Show competition, uneven pace when approaching an obstacle, and generally erratic behavior have persisted to a noticeable degree despite five or six years of rest alternated with remedial work. He will jump predictably and reasonably well over familiar obstacles not exceeding three feet six inches in height for a familiar rider; however, he is highly unreliable (if not impossible) to jump under any other conditions, and does display some nervous agitation even under familiar conditions—i.e. a lot of nervous pawing, inability to relax or to stand quietly, increased respiration, heartbeat, and sweating without direct physical cause. As a control, he has been successfully trained in other and equally difficult sequences of signal and response, and performs them smoothly, predictably, with no waste motion or observable agitation. I have noted no significant alterations in his pasture or stable behavior; although he has shown an increased resistance to being saddled over these years.

Pip is a small animal between three and four years old who is receiving his early handling and training from a young man who is himself just learning. I was recently called into the training paddock to assist; my job being to hold Pip while the young trainer got on his back, and then to act as an extra control while Pip walked (we hoped) about the paddock with the weight on his back. I found an animal whose posture and behavior showed extreme tension and instability. He stood rigid, tense, eyes wide open and rolling, nostrils flaring, general muscular twitching at irregular intervals, rapid breathing, and greatly accelerated heartbeat. Further, although Pip is a small animal, it was almost impossible to hold him from bolting away when movements were made toward getting on his back. I know this animal's pasture and barn behavior is consistently relaxed, and that he is quietly amenable to the handling received about the stable, i.e., grooming, feeding, watering, being led, etc. I questioned the trainer concerning his procedure to find that several steps had been omitted or hurried over—preliminary handling period, gradual exposure to saddle, establishment of stable responses to signals and/or commands for moving ahead and stopping were the most important omissions. I suggested that the missing ground be quietly and systematically reworked, and gave some constructive supervision in accomplishing this. Two weeks later I was pleased to note Pip stand relaxed while the saddle was placed, walk, quietly into the paddock following his young trainer, and respond quietly, alertly, and consistently to his trainer's signals and/or commands. The animal now was alert, interested, predictable, and responsive in the identical situation where two weeks previously he had been tense, fearful, and almost uncontrollable. Further, the former situation was not a new one for the animal. It seems that the fearful, unresponsive behavior in the training paddock had been repeated at least six times before I observed it and suggested the successful, remedial procedures. I think the clear change in this animal's behavior can be attributed mainly to the handling and training methods which preceded it in each case—*methods that were substantially the same excepting the rate at which their content was given in each case.*

Chapter V

Stress and Emotion

STIMULUS implies measurement, but in observing behavior measurement should express meaning. What does the stimulus to which the animal responds mean for that animal? What is its significance for him, personally, or as a member of a species? These questions lead us to the core of the problem of the relation between stress and emotion.

This subject first attracted our attention in 1927. One of our sheep, as previously related, developed an experimental neurosis during the course of what we then regarded as simple conditioning. The training routine seemed so innocuous that we were at a loss to account for the animal's sudden and dramatic emotional upset. It finally dawned upon us that stress meant one thing to us but something quite different to the animal. The conditioning routine which we regarded as innocuous apparently meant murder to the sheep.

Since Cannon's classical studies of the cat's emergency reaction to the menace of a barking dog, the medical journals have been inundated by a flood of articles on the physiology of stress. The highly technical details need not concern us here but basic principles do. In the modern laboratory the stresses commonly employed are such as may most easily be controlled and reproduced; for example, extreme cold, forced exercise on a treadmill, electric shocks and the like. It is supposed that the animal acting as a computing machine calculates the sum of these stresses and reacts at the appropriate intensity.

In the physiological laboratory and especially where the subjects are animals all goes well. Trouble begins when the physician attempts to apply this simple formulation to the circumstances of daily living. When he is confronted by a patient incapacitated by intense, faulty, or long enduring emergency reactions, he is tempted to indulge in a semantic *tour de force* and to extend the list of possible stresses to include business worries, social loss of face, bereavement, and so on. Thus in attempting to alleviate his patient's distress the physician's ingenuity is taxed by his attempts to identify or imagine the stresses at work.

In such cases it is not a matter of scientific integrity but rather of the futility of attempting to apply a simple physiological formulation of the stress reaction in animals to disorders of human personality and behavior. The work of the bodily organs must be integrated with observed behavior in any effective clinical investigation of the role of stress in human emotional incapacity or illness.

This clinically more adequate conception of the relation between stress and emotion has been designated by John Whitehorn as the *acute emotional experience*. Because of its historical importance, his own statement follows.

"The primary focus of attention in this discussion of emotion is 'the acute emotional experience,' by which I mean to designate a biological condition, characterized subjectively as an excited, tense feeling with considerable tendency to act, but with some uncertainty as to what to do, and characterized objectively by motor restlessness or activity, not smoothly patterned, with indications of excess effort, as shown in the facial and respiratory musculature, tremor of voice and of skeleto-muscular action, together with sudden changes in visceral activity. . . . This experience is found, in general, to be unpleasant and those who experience it in intense degree, may well wonder what is the use of such a thing. It is confusing, disorienting disruptive of the smooth, habitual, integrative modes of behavior—apparently most unphysiological. Yet, when viewed in a larger time span, we may note, not infrequently, that such experiences have been followed by significant improvement in the adjustment to life.

"I would postulate, for these and other reasons, that the acute emotional experience has, as its biological function, the precipitation of an internal crisis, in which habit is interrupted and the more raw or primitive facilities for biological adjustments are summoned up—not merely sugar for energy production and hastened circulation for increased oxygen use, but also the neural capacities of the organism for forming new associations between reaction and situation and for reorganizing behavior. These latter are the resources which we recognize as intelligence—the capacity which might lie latent and unused if not activated by an emotional experience. . . . In postulating such a function for the acute emotional experience, one must admit that, in life, its purpose is not always successfully achieved. By rigid conditions, it is possible experimentally, to produce predicaments which elicit acute emotional experiences whose resolution is blocked by inhibitory training, and thus to reduce the functional value of emotion, transforming it, so to speak, into the condition of disability and distress which we call anxiety, chronic or recurrent."

Now back to the sheep. After a brief period of basic training in conditioning, when it is being led to the laboratory, its physiological preparation for the daily test has already begun. It is in the grip of the acute emotional experience that Whitehorn describes. Due to its inhibitory training, however, no means are available for resolving, or escaping from, its disturbing state. Although its deportment is composed and it does not resist the leash, it is, nevertheless, passing into a state of anxious expectation which will steadily increase until it is released from the laboratory at the end of the test. While quietly submitting to the experimenter's preparations, it maintains a state of quiet watchfulness or vigilance. If the sheep could verbalize, it would be constantly asking itself: "What are today's questions going to be and will I know the answers?"

The sheep has been brought into *a situation of stress*. It was earlier referred to as *a situation of origin* in which after a time, the experimental neurosis will be precipitated. We cannot profitably think of this situation of stress as a sum of specific stressers to be identified and measured, as stimuli are measured by the physiologist. It is the *meaning* of the laboratory situation for a particular animal at a specific time during the history of its conditioning that makes this environment stressful. A simple experiment performed some years ago supports the validity of this point of view.

A sheep was brought daily to the laboratory and subjected repeatedly to the sound of a door buzzer followed inevitably by shock to the foreleg. A continuous kymograph record was made of head and foreleg movement, respiration and heart beat (by means of a cardiotachometer). During the daily test, ten buzzer signals were given at intervals of one to three minutes.

At the end of one hundred signals, each followed by shock, all signals and shocks were omitted but the usual recording was continued as before. Each day the animal came to the laboratory and took its place in the restraining harness. The experimenter adjusted the recording apparatus but did nothing further. At the end of the hour the sheep was released and rejoined the flock. During the two months of daily reassurance that nothing was to disturb it during the test period the sheep visibly relaxed its pose of tense watchfulness. Restless movement diminished, breathing became slow and regular, and the heart rate gradually slowed. At the end of this "do nothing" regimen, the animal in its restraining harness had by its quiet and relaxed deportment begun to suggest itself as a suitable subject for determining basal metabolic rate.

The situation of stress had acquired the meaning of a situation of relaxation. The two months of reassurance in the laboratory had diametrically changed the meaning of its work place. The sheep's surroundings were now interpreted by it as reassuring rather than alarming.

But now at the beginning of what the sheep must

have interpreted as just another do-nothing day in the laboratory the door buzzed sounded for ten seconds but *without shock*. The result was a violent explosion of leaping and struggling which continued throughout the period with no further signals or shocks. In terms of the violence of the sheep's reaction to the familiar buzzer, *this formerly mild, stressful signal had now suddenly taken on the meaning of a gravely threatening stresser*. In other words, the laboratory situation had once again (and this time suddenly) changed its meaning for the sheep. Once again it had become a situation of stress.

To return to our sheep awaiting its first signal of the day. As we have mentioned, it is already in the grip of a generalized excitement or acute emotional experience. (We need not be too finicky to allow ourselves to speak of the sheep's experience.) The longer it is forced to wait, the more intense its physiological preparation for any specific emergency that may arise. The first conditioned stimulus or signal, be it positive or negative, ushers in just such a specific emergency. The first click of the metronome, if that is the signal, elicits a sharp spike of apprehension or vigilance. In Robert's case the metronome clicking once a second for a few seconds was followed by shock. Paradoxically, however, the brisk, forced flexion of his foreleg evoked by this brief, mild electrical stimulus gave him, under these circumstances, an abrupt emotional let-down. The shock is here a *relaxer,* not a *stresser*. On the other hand an unsignalled, and hence unexpected shock is a brief but definite threat and, therefore, *a stresser*. Thus, *the same, precisely measur-*

able stimulus, the electric shock, may be either a stresser or a relaxer, depending upon its specific meaning for the sheep.

This statement applies, of course, to the goat as well and can be illustrated by an experiment. In the course of a year of practice one of our goats developed a longer and longer delayed conditioned response to the metronome clicking once a second. Finally, it became accustomed to the signal sounding for 100 seconds before the shock. It would then delay flexion until the metronome had been clicking for at least 85 seconds.

In this experiment we were employing a cardiotachometer for the purpose of correlating the degree of stress with the heart-rate. As the metronome clicked, the heart accelerated, then slowed, then accelerated again at the next click and continued accelerating along a saw-tooth type of curve. At the hundredth second when the animal received the shock, its heart-rate abruptly dropped to the presignal level within two seconds, so sudden was the relaxing effect of its forced reaction to this shock. On the other hand, the same goat waiting in a state of tense expectancy during a long pause between signals received an unsignalled shock of the same intensity as that following the usual 100 second sounding of the metronome. Its heart raced instantly and took 15 to 20 seconds to slow down. *The shock in the former case was a relaxer but the same shock in the latter case was a stresser.* We cannot afford to be rigidly mechanistic in thinking about the experimenter's quantitative control of the stressful stimuli. It is the behavioral meaning of the given stimulus when applied to the animal which is of basic significance.

Since all types of Pavlovian conditioning develop in the animal increasingly rigid control of its emotional reactions to danger *all conditioning is difficult conditioning* and will, if long continued, lead to emotional disaster. However, this approach to disaster can be hastened by one or a combination of conditioning procedures discussed in a previous chapter.

When the animal comes, through its conditioning in the laboratory, to impose restraint upon itself, it is no longer a free agent. Then, if the experimenter subjects it to the hazards of monotony, confusion, or overstimulation, the development of various emotional incapacities can be confidently expected and looked for. Their onset may be sudden but is usually, as we now believe, both insidious and slow. We have come to recognize in our animals three clearly distinguishable signs foretelling the approaching "nervous breakdown." Let us choose the sheep for illustration.

First of all, the sheep enters upon a stage of prophylactic caution in which its movements in the laboratory are markedly restricted and deliberate. It has become a perfectionist. It seems as if it feared to do the wrong thing. What we may infer to be similar behavior in man under threatening circumstances is portrayed by Emilio Mira y Lopez:

"Prudence and Self Restraint: Observed from without, the subject appears modest, prudent, and unpretending. By means of voluntary self-restraint he limits his aims and ambitions, and renounces all those pleasures which entail risk or exposure. The individual in this stage is already under the inhibitory influence of fear. He reacts with a prophylactic avoidance of the

approaching situation. *Introspectively,* the subject is not yet conscious of being afraid. On the contrary, he is rather self-satisfied and proud because he considers himself endowed with greater foresight than other human beings."

Next, under the stress of daily conditioning a stage of oscillating emotional behavior supervenes in which, at the experimenter's signals the sheep is thrown into a state of rigid immobility. At later signals, however, the animal reverses itself and responds explosively with vehement movements often resembling aggressive behavior. On one occasion, a middle-aged and formerly inoffensive ewe snatched off the experimenter's spectacles as he knelt to attach the electrodes to her foreleg.

During these phases of prophylactic caution and of oscillating immobility and aggressiveness it is as if the precise motor patterns developed during basic training had been inundated by strong tides of emotion.

Later, after long-continued wear and tear of conditioning although the sheep's behavior may appear to have become stabilized, its deportment in the laboratory has subtly altered and now appears to the experimenter as "peculiar" or "unfamiliar." At this point the animal is rapidly approaching the precipice of emotional breakdown.

The above account of the three premonitory signs of an approaching full-blown experimental neurosis is, almost certainly, oversimplified. Since our disillusionment concerning the "normality" of our best demonstration animals, Robert and Brown Billy, as previously related, we do not at present know which of our many thoroughly conditioned sheep and goats are "normal" and which are "disturbed." We do know, however, that all of our conditioning procedures are stressful and will, if continued, lead to behavioral incapacities of one kind or another in the experimental animal forced by its self-imposed restraint to submit to them.

The direct comparison of the emotional behavior of man with that of sheep and goat, which will be attempted in the next chapter, is based upon the conviction shared by those of us who have spent some years investigating animal behavior with medical intent. This conviction has been stated by K. S. Lashley:

"Fundamental patterns of emotional reaction and tempermental types seem to have undergone little change in mammalian evolution. The major changes are rather the result of development of intelligent foresight and the inhibition of action in anticipation of more remote prospects."

Chapter VI

The Emotional Basis of Mental Health

SELF-IMPOSED restraint, not of the individual's choosing, has been the central topic of our earlier discussion. A gloomy prospect indeed. This gloom was somewhat dissipated by one cheerful example. The performing seal in the circus seems, from his zestful barking, to be enjoying his work. Even though compelled to travel in a cage from town to town and to perform on schedule at his trainers' signals, he is still a free agent.

Less cheerful examples are found in situations of military combat. The soldier *subjecting himself* to severe restraints must endure, often for long periods, the hazards of loneliness, monotony, confusion, and overstimulation. To these are often added severe deprivations and hardships including exhaustion and pain. Under such conditions his emotional reactions are surprisingly similar to those of our sheep and goats subjected to arduous conditioning.

In the fall of 1952* we were given the opportunity to interview officers and men at the Sasebo Replacement Depot in Japan. They had completed their period of service in Korea and were about to board ship for home. Later, we spent a brief period in Korea

* Under the auspices of the Johns Hopkins University Operations Research Office operating under Contract with the Department of the Army.

at a mobile army surgical hospital unit near the central front and visited other medical installations in the combat area.

Our casual interviews and conversations with men who had combat experience were not limited by formalities of military rank, since we had none. We took pains, moreover, to avoid asking leading questions. Accompanying chaplains on their visits to the wounded and discussing our material with medical officers were both profitable experiences.

In the combat zone the front line is a place of menace even when all is quiet. It was the consensus among officers and men that a soldier coming up to the front line (MLR) for the first time should, where possible, be allowed ten days for becoming emotionally adjusted. A common expression was "levelling off." After ten days the new man might safely be given an assignment of extra hazard. Presumably, the exercise of his combat skills would, after this brief habituation, be less impeded by the viscosity of his emotional reactions.

The stress of remaining day and night at the front is markedly increased by the onset of intense artillery fire. Does this barrage signal attack and when will it come? Or again, if relief has been promised and does not arrive, painfully uncertain expectation is still further increased. Soldiers with experience in combat said that they had come to recognize certain premonitory signs of emotional difficulty in men exposed to the combat situation. Without prompting, they clearly described *the same signs* that our animals exhibit preceding emotional breakdown.

Both sheep and soldier may enter upon the state of prophylactic caution previously described. The soldier at the front line during his last month of duty before returning home may exhibit excessive caution. The opinion was often expressed that because of this involuntary and excessive carefulness he should not, the military situation permitting, be sent on patrol or given any other assignment of extra hazard. Through the exercise of undue caution he might endanger not only his own life but that of other members of his patrol.

Oscillations of emotional behavior are often seen in the soldier going into combat for the first time. One lieutenant had observed when leading new men on their first mission that when they made their first contact with the enemy, all wanted to go forward with little regard for leadership. He had found this initial aggressiveness to be characteristic. Other officers corroborated his observations by having noted the random aggression of the inexperienced soldier as evidenced by his firing in a "trigger-happy" fashion. When this impulsive, aggressive phase is terminated by the officer's orders, the soldier may not be able to get going again. At first he can't stop and when stopped he can't start. On later missions the new men become battle-wise. They are more deliberate and look to leadership more. During these phases of prophylactic caution and of oscillating aggressiveness and immobility it is as if the precise skills developed by the recruit during his basic training were now, as in the case of our sheep, being inundated by emotion.

Later, after long continued wear and tear of life in

the combat zone and repeated combat experiences, although the soldier may appear to be stable, his friends will notice that his behavior has subtly altered and now appears to them as "peculiar" or "unfamiliar."

A sergeant had gone on about thirty patrols, many involving combat. He knew his small group from training days so well that he could see in two or three cases that a particular soldier "could not take" another patrol. Asked to specify, he said it was their unfamiliar behavior—not taking a joke, irritability, aimless activity, talking too much or being unusually quiet. His observations were fully confirmed by others.

In sharp contrast to our sheep and goats under stress of conditioning, the soldier can call upon resources for ameliorating the well-nigh intolerable stresses often encountered at the front, on patrol or in combat. These resources are provided by his previous indoctrination and present leadership. Both are too pervasive and complex in their influence upon the day-to-day emotional status of the soldier to be adequately discussed here.

Since man is both animal and idealist, it follows that during basic training and later, it is possible for the soldier to develop a simple and sturdy military ideal. By means of this ideal he can anchor his behavior to the values of "being able to take it," loyalty and obedience. His stability and reliability as a soldier are governed in large part by this moral mechanism. For example the ideal of "being able to take it" appeared during our interviews at Sasebo. These combat veterans, one and all, denied having experienced loss of appetite, nausea or loss of weight. It was discovered in Korea, however, that loss of appetite, digestive upsets and so forth were not uncommon. This *favorable forgetfulness* (the psychoanalyst's pedantic expression is "retrospective falsification") of soldiers on their way back home demonstrates the sturdiness of this ideal of being able to take it.

The military ideal of loyalty is repeatedly displayed by the numerous cases of severe anxiety attacks brought on by a soldier's inability to save a wounded comrade's life. Combat stresses arouse unsatisfied needs for safety and comfort. These needs have negative goals—to get away from something painful or unpleasant. Techniques of leadership enable the officer to counterbalance these negative goals by positive ones. By briefing, or otherwise, he may arouse strong positive motivation for accomplishing a mission. Pride in belonging to the outfit, and "we have done it once, we can do it again."

We believe it is not unscientific to recognize that problems of indoctrination and leadership are moral problems. In attempting to understand how the soldier successfully masters fear and pain in combat his religious experience, formalized or not, is as indispensable a datum as palpitation, labored breathing or the hollow, all-gone feelings from his insides.

But what about zest? What about joy, or even fun? All of these contribute to the emotional basis of mental health and it should concern us to discover why they are so often almost completely absent or appear in such crippled or grotesquely distorted forms.

Of high spirits and cheerfulness Darwin wrote: "From the excitment of pleasure, the circulation becomes more rapid; the eyes are bright, and the color of the face rises. The brain, being stimulated by the increased flow of blood, reacts on the mental powers; lively ideas pass still more rapidly through the mind, and the affections are warmed. I heard a child, a little under four years old, when asked what was meant by being in good spirits, answer, 'It is laughing, talking, and kissing.' It would be difficult to give a truer and more practical definition."

The little child, as well as the man, has the need of being a free agent and of expressing himself. L. van der Horst of Amsterdam in describing the drawings of children says: "One of our children, a boy aged four years and two months, was drawing an immense number of circles; during this persevering occupation he was asked what he was drawing. He answered, 'I don't know; it isn't finished yet.' After a short time he made a number of dots in each circle and cried in triumph, 'Biscuits with sugared caraway seeds.' "

Economics was called the dismal science when it sought to rob human behavior of its appropriate values. John Stuart Mill long ago complained that the pursuit of wealth is impeded by man's "aversion to labor" and his "desire of the present enjoyment of costly indulgencies." Is psychosomatic medicine to become our contemporary dismal science? More than a decade ago John Whitehorn wrote:

"The medical profession has a tendency to look upon emotion as morbid. Indeed, in recent years, so much is being said about pathological somatic conditions attributed to emotion, one might almost believe that emotions are to take the place of germs as the enemy in the next great medical campaign for health."

Today stress is the watchword. We have a physiology of stress, "diseases of adaptation" precipitated by enduring stress, and a stress sociology. Every morning one may hear morbidly oriented hints for good health in which he is exhorted to perpetual vigilance about overweight, high blood pressure, cancer and the rest.

In this pervasive atmosphere of tension and gloom to embark upon a discussion of the rational pursuit of pleasure may seem an anachronism. It is as if one were to speak of the technique of playing the lute. Nevertheless, we propose to consider pleasure—its biology and its medical importance.

Our previous studies of sheep and goat behavior had been concerned with the animal's ability to find its way through an out-of-door maze. Even when the sheep or goat was unable to learn to find its way through this labyrinth, it remained placid and no nervous disturbances were at any time observed. However, when the animal was subjected to the mild restraint of the conditioning harness, neurotic disturbances became the rule during difficult or prolonged conditioning.

The simplest explanation of the sheep's placid acceptance of its inadequacy to learn the maze as contrasted with its neurotic breakdown when faced with a too difficult conditioning problem seemed to be a matter of initiative. In the maze the animal set its own pace and could give up and lie down if it chose. In the conditioning harness the experimenter gave the signals at *his* pleasure and administered or withheld the appropriate "reward" or "punishment." The sheep unable confidently to predict what was to happen next could only "sweat it out."

But what can the experimental biology of behavior contribute to our understanding of pleasure? Psychiatrists, preoccupied with states of continuing pain and fear in their patients have naturally and justifiably turned to the researches of Cannon and Pavlov for biological orientation. In this area of research the emphasis is on stress and bodily mobilization for emergency. The biology of relaxation and pleasurable consequences of repeated success in the exercise of skills have, on the other hand, been relatively neglected.

Some years ago Sandor Rado introduced a conception of pleasure organization. According to him, man in the exercise of pleasure functions derives excitation from stimulating the sensitive spots available in his mind and body. "These pleasure functions," he continues, "interact and combine with one another to make up the individual's entire pleasure organization. The latter is obviously neither sexual nor nonsexual, but an entity of a new order brought about by integration on a higher level. It undergoes typical changes during the life cycle, and is characterized at every stage by a measure of functional flexibility, working in the service of one and then another of the biological systems. . . . This pleasure organization requires a term that reflects its biological nature and avoids confusion between the superior entity and its component parts."

Music offers an illustration of this thesis. The

singer, for example, uses his breathing apparatus for aesthetic expression but in the case of the violinist the aesthetic function of the breathing mechanism is displaced to the bow arm. As the violin teacher tells his pupil, "You must breathe with your bow."

A few years ago a study of preliterate deaf children from two-and-a-half to five years was in progress at Public School 47 in New York. A former colleague of ours, Joseph Church, who participated in the investigation, was impressed by the vitality of the urge in these children to develop pleasure patterns which seemed to compensate for their sensory handicap. For example, a little boy experimented almost endlessly with rhythmic tactile patterns achieved by drawing a pointer across a row of vertical wooden rods first rapidly then slowly. A little girl made a pleasure ritual of washing the children's juice cups, luxuriating in the feel of the warm, soapy water. Van der Horst's sprightly little boy persevering in the fun of drawing circles was up to the same game.

As usual, let us return to the laboratory. Upon being awarded the Nobel Prize, Pavlov concluded his brief remarks with the words: "Only one thing in life is of actual interest for us—our psychical experience. Its mechanism, however, has been, and remains, wrapped in deep mystery. All human resources —art, religion, literature, philosophy, historical science—all these unite to cast a beam of light into this mysterious darkness. Man has at his disposal one more powerful ally—biological science with its strictly objective methods."

These words portray Pavlov as he was from first to last—the uncompromising and aggressive idealist.

His gifted pupil (and an equally intransigent ideal-ist), Professor P. S. Kupolov, wrote us, when the siege of Leningrad had been lifted, of an experiment which he was just undertaking.

The hungry dog (and, says Kupalov, the dog is always hungry) comes to the experimental room where through previous training he knows what to expect. In one corner of the room is a table (A) to which a door buzzer is fastened. When the buzzer sounds, the dog jumps on the table and finds a small portion of food. In another corner is table (B) pro-vided with a metronome set to click once a second. When this metronome starts, the dog jumps on table B and gets his bit of food. Placed on a shelf (C) on the wall is another metronome set to click twice a second. When the metronome on the shelf sounds, the dog finds food on neither table. The set procedure day after day is a signal from A, B, or C in random order but a signal is given every three minutes. The dog has no respite. Every three minutes a decision must be made. He must go to table A or to table B or if the metronome on shelf C clicks, he is to do nothing since this is a no food signal.

After the dog has become accustomed to this mo-notonous and unavoidable procedure for some time, a small rug is placed on the floor in the center of the room. If he happens to be sitting or lying on this rug, all signals will cease and he can take his ease. When he has learned to control his environment through the use of this rug, he has *an instrument of freedom*.

Can we not discover such a magic carpet for our-selves? Perhaps even with our present limited knowl-edge of the therapeutic uses of hopes and pleasures

we might safely predict that in many cases member-
ship in an amateur string quartet might serve as a
magic carpet and be more efficacious than ACTH, or
that going fishing might be better therapy than cortisone.

Finally, a few words about the self-perpetuating
neurotic process which may so severely curtail its vic-
tim in his striving to be a free agent. Our contemporary conformities, with the mechanization of thought
and feeling they impose, enhance the baleful operations of the neurotic process in thwarting the strivings
of the human spirit. But every individual possesses a
secret weapon with which to combat neurosis and
gain freedom. That weapon is the creative impulse,
which provides vigor and enchantment; buoyancy
and elegance; or incisiveness of thought and flexibility of spirit, whichever pair of terms one may
choose. Perhaps all should be included. From our
point of view, it is this creative impulse which gen-
erates zest and insures mental health.

Selected References from 1926 to 1955

1926. LIDDELL, H. S. and SIMPSON, E. D.: A preliminary study of motor conditioned reflexes in thyroidectomized sheep. *Proc. Soc. Exper. Biol. & Med., 23*:720, 1926.

1927. LIDDELL, H. S. and BAYNE, T. L.: The development of experimental neurasthenia in the sheep during the formation of difficult conditioned reflexes. *Am. J. Physiol., 81*:494, 1927.

1928. PAVLOV, I. P.: *Lectures on Conditioned Reflexes.* Trans. Gantt, W. Horsley. New York, International Publishers, 1928. (Translator's preface: W. Horsley Gantt, Leningrad, September 1, 1928.)

1935. ANDERSON, O. D. and LIDDELL, H. S.: Observations on experimental neurosis in sheep. *Arch. Neurol. & Psychiat., 34*:330, 1935.

1935. LIDDELL, H. S., ANDERSON, O. D., KOTYUKA, E. and HARTMAN, F. A.: The effect of extract of adrenal cortex on experimental neurosis in sheep. *Arch. Neurol. & Psychiat., 34*:973, 1935.

1938. ROSE, J. A., TAINTON-POTTBERG, A. and ANDERSON, O. D.: Effects of insulin shock on behavior and conditioned reflex action in the well trained sheep. *Proc. Soc. Exper. Biol. & Med., 38*:635, 1938.

1939. ANDERSON, O. D., PARMENTER, RICHARD and LIDDELL, H. S.: Some cardiovascular manifestations of the experimental neurosis in sheep. *Psychosom. Med., 1*:93, 1939.

1941. ANDERSON, O. D. and PARMENTER, RICHARD: A long-term study of the experimental neurosis in the sheep and dog. *Psychosom. Med. Mon. II:* III and IV, 1941.

1942. LIDDELL, H. S.: The alteration of instinctual processes through the influence of conditioned reflexes. *Psychosom. Med., 4:*390, 1942.

1944. GANTT, W. HORSLEY: *Experimental Basis for Neurotic Behavior.* New York, Hoeber, 1944.

1950. LIDDELL, H. S.: *The Role of Vigilance in the Development of Animal Neurosis, Anxiety.* Edit. Hoch, Paul and Zubin, Joseph. New York, Grune and Stratton, 1950, p. 183.

1950. LIDDELL, H. S.: *Animal Origins of Anxiety. Feelings and Emotions.* Edit. Reymert, Martin L., New York, McGraw-Hill, 1950, p. 181.

1950. LIDDELL, H. S.: Specific factors that modify tolerance for environmental stress. Life stress and bodily disease. Edit. Wolff, H. G. *Research Publ. A. Nerv. & Ment. Dis.,* 1950, Chap. X.

1951. LIDDELL, H. S.: *The Influence of Experimental Neuroses on the Respiratory Function. Treatment of Asthma.* Edit. Abramson, Harold A. Baltimore, Williams & Wilkins, 1951, Chap. 6, p. 126.

1952. LIDDELL, H. S.: *Experimental Induction of Psychoneuroses by Conditional Reflex with Stress. The Biology of Mental Health and Disease.* The twenty-seventh annual conference of the Milbank Memorial Fund. New York, Hoeber, 1952, Chap. 29, p. 498.

1952. LIDDELL, H. S.: Effect of corticosteroids in experimental psychoneurosis. The biology of mental health and disease. New York Hoeber, 1950. Chap. 36, p. 591.

1954. LIDDELL, H. S.: Conditioning and emotions. *Scientific American,* January, 1954.

1955. LIDDELL, H. S.: The natural history of neurotic behavior. *Society and Medicine.* Edit. Galdston, Iago. Number XVIII of the New York Academy of Medicine. Lectures to the laity. International Universities Press. New York, 1955.

1955. BLAUVELT, HELEN: *Dynamics of the Mother-Newborn Relationship in Goats.* Group Processes, transactions of the first conference, September 26, 27, 28, 29 and 30, 1954. Sponsored by the Josiah Macy, Jr. Foundation, New York, N.Y., 1955, p. 221.

This Book

EMOTIONAL HAZARDS IN ANIMALS AND MAN

By

Howard S. Liddell, Ph.D.

was set, printed and bound by the George Banta Company, Inc. of Menasha, Wisconsin. The page trim size is 5½ x 8½ inches. The type page is 21 x 37 picas. The type face is Linotype Baskerville, set 11 point on 13 point. The text paper is 70 lb. white Winnebago Eggshell. The cover is Pajco Lexide, No. 25, Embossing 32, Finish TT Black.

With THOMAS BOOKS *careful attention is given to all details of manufacturing and design. It is the Publisher's desire to present books that are satisfactory as to their physical qualities and artistic possibilities and appropriate for their particular use.* THOMAS BOOKS *will be true to those laws of quality that assure a good name and good will.*